Moola Bandha
The Master Key

D0962422

With kind regards, ॐ and prem

Swami Niranjan

Moola Bandha

The Master Key

Swami Buddhananda

Under the Guidance of
Swami Satyananda Saraswati

Yoga Publications Trust, Munger, Bihar, India

Published by Bihar School of Yoga
    First edition 1978
    Reprinted 1984
    Second edition 1996
    Reprinted 1998

Published by Yoga Publications Trust
    Reprinted 2000, 2001, 2002, 2004, 2006, 2007

ISBN: 978-81-85787-32-9

Publisher and distributor: Yoga Publications Trust, Ganga Darshan, Munger, Bihar, India.

Website: www.biharyoga.net

Printed at Thomson Press (India) Limited, New Delhi, 110001

Dedication

*In humility we offer this dedication to
Swami Sivananda Saraswati, who initiated
Swami Satyananda Saraswati into the secrets of yoga.*

Contents

The Three Bandhas

In the Yogataravali Sutras it is said: "Jalandhara bandha, uddiyana bandha and moola bandha are situated in the throat, abdomen and perineum respectively. If their duration can be increased then where is the fear of death? By the practice of these three bandhas the dormant kundalini awakens and enters into the sushumna. The breath becomes still (*kumbhaka*). With the performance of these three bandhas the *rechaka* (exhalation) and *pooraka* (inhalation) ceases to function. With this the senses become purified and *kevala* (enlightenment) takes place. I pray for that *vidya* (knowledge) residing in *kevala kumbhaka*." (YS, 5,6,8)

The word *bandha* (which should not to be confused with the words *bandh, baddha* and *bandhana,* which have similar meanings) may be defined in several ways. A Sanskrit dictionary definition runs as follows: 'binding, tying a bond, tie, chain, fetter, a ligature, to catch, hold captive, arrest, imprison, fix, fasten, hold back, restrain, stop, shut, close, to redirect, check, obstruct, clot and lock.'

Bandha may also be defined analogously and is likened to the 'damming of a river', 'building a bridge' or 'building over the sea'. This can be interpreted as meaning that a bandha is a vehicle to traverse the ocean of *samsara*, worldly existence, and to reach the other shore of enlightenment.

The bandha group consists of moola, uddiyana and jalandhara bandhas. The fourth, maha bandha, is a

1

combination of these three. How is it that a group of only four practices is considered equal to or of greater importance than the hundreds of asana, pranayama and mudra practices and their variations? Traditionally, the fact that the spiritual aspirant was introduced to bandhas secretly and only after he had mastered the execution of many, often complex, asanas, pranayamas and mudras shows that the practice of bandhas was highly respected by yogic practitioners.

Seen physically, moola bandha is the conscious, wilful contraction of the perineum or cervix, uddiyana bandha of the solar plexus and jalandhara bandha of the throat.

The concept of lock

In most modern yogic literature bandha is defined simply as a 'lock'. However, the true meaning of bandha is essentially paradoxical, for it is said that by locking or contracting certain muscles on the physical level a subtle process of 'unlocking' goes on simultaneously on mental and pranic levels. Most modern muscle relaxation therapies advocate that by the total, systematic contraction and relaxation of muscles all over the body, one regains complete physical and mental relaxation. The underlying rationale of such a theory is that in order to remove physical and mental tension it is more effective to first learn to exaggerate the tension already existing in the body by wilfully and selectively contracting all of its muscles.

Bandhas work in a similar way, simultaneously affecting the physical, pranic, mental, psychic and causal bodies. They have far reaching effects because they are associated with energy centres in the spine and brain. Therefore, bandhas are more dynamic, explosive and immediate in effect than simple contractions of muscles in the arms or legs.

The mechanics of bandhas

Bandhas involve the contraction or squeezing of muscles. As there are three bandhas, there are three main muscle groups involved: perineal muscles, abdominal muscles and cervical (neck) muscles. Contraction of these muscles affects the nervous, circulatory, respiratory, endocrine and energy systems. When a muscle is contracted a nerve impulse is relayed to the brain, triggering other neuronal circuits and nervous centres. This in turn affects our state of consciousness. In response to this stimulation the brain adjusts its firing patterns. For example:

Moola bandha (perineal contraction) stimulates both the sensory-motor and the autonomic nervous systems in the pelvic region. When moola bandha is performed, pelvic stimulation activates parasympathetic fibres emerging from the pelvic spinal cord. Parasympathetic fibres emerge from the cervical (neck) and sacral (pelvic) areas only, while sympathetic fibres emerge from the thoracic (upper back) and lumbar (lower back) areas. The performance of bandhas has been experimentally shown to enforce all parasympathetic activities in the body which includes a decrease in: heart rate, respiration and blood pressure (only in an individual with normal blood pressure), and a general sense of rest and relaxation.[1] Sympathetic nervous stimulation also occurs in moola bandha but at a subdued level. The overall effect of stimulating both parasympathetic and sympathetic nervous systems is to rebalance these two major components of nervous activity in the body. This has very definite repercussions on the hypothalamus (responsible for the complete endocrine system) which relays its information to the whole limbic (emotional) system and the cerebral cortex (outer layer of the brain).

Uddiyana bandha (abdominal contraction) compresses the digestive organs, adrenal glands, kidneys, and most important the solar plexus. This 'brain-in-the-stomach' is squeezed and in return a flood of energy is generated in the abdomen and chest. The energy has healing qualities and is experienced consciously as beneficial, enhancing our sense of wellbeing. Uddiyana bandha tones the sympathetic nervous system, encouraging it to work more efficiently. It also enables us to gain control over the sympathetic nervous system so that it does not function in inappropriate situations, thus avoiding the effects of stress and anxiety in psychosomatic disease.

Jalandhara bandha (throat compression) stretches the neck, pulling the spinal cord and thus the brain. This has subtle effects on the pituitary and pineal glands while the forward flexion (in jalandhara bandha the chin is placed on the chest) affects the thyroid, parathyroid and thymus glands. At the same time it stimulates the parasympathetic spinal area in the medulla oblongata (situated at the bottom of the brain and the top of the spinal cord) regulating heart rate, respiration, blood pressure, etc. Finally, jalandhara bandha also compresses the carotid sinuses which help in lowering the blood pressure. By reducing sympathetic tone, one achieves a sense of rest, relaxation and general wellbeing.

The performance of bandhas leads to a general massaging effect of the muscles and internal organs. Increased blood supply to these areas aids in general purification of the body. Bandhas affect the endocrine glands. As these glands are intimately related to the chakras, it is a natural consequence that the bandhas also affect the chakras. When stimulated, the chakras influence every aspect of the organism, revitalizing it with life-sustaining energy.

The physical effects of bandhas

The performance of bandhas in conjunction with pranayama (breath and energy control) affects the whole body as follows:
- They harmonize the efficient functioning of the endocrine system: jalandhara directly influences the pituitary, pineal, thyroid, parathyroid, thymus; uddiyana bandha directly influences the adrenals and pancreas; moola bandha directly influences the gonads and the perineal body/ cervix (which are said to be vestigial endocrine glands). All bandhas have an indirect effect on the pituitary, pineal and brain.
- As a result of the direct effect that bandhas have on the endocrine glands, certain biorhythms in the body are

also regulated. For example, both moola bandha and uddiyana bandha are extremely useful in stabilizing menstrual periods.

- All bandhas, when performed correctly, lower respiration rate, inducing calmness and relaxation.[2]
- Blood pressure is decreased.
- Heart rate is lessened.
- Alpha brainwave production, an index of profound relaxation, is increased, indicating slowing of nervous activity.
- Sympathetic activity in the body is decreased, a further index of relaxation.
- Confused and/or crossed neuronal circuits in the brain are reordered, in effect 'retraining the brain'.
- The digestive system is toned, massaged and revitalized via pressure on the internal organs.
- Harmony in the activity of the urogenital system occurs as a result of reflex action via the nervous system.

The pranic effects of bandhas

Each bandha is associated with the stimulation of a specific focus of prana. Bandhas are said to be mutually related to certain nerve plexes in the spine, the endocrine glands; as well as pranic energy centres known as chakras. For each nerve plexus and endocrine gland on the physical level there exists a corresponding chakra on the pranic level as follows: *mooladhara* – sacral/coccygeal plexus; *swadhisthana* – prostatic plexus; *manipura* – solar plexus; *anahata* – cardiac plexus; *vishuddhi* – pharyngeal/laryngeal plexus; for *ajna* and *sahasrara*, the pineal/pituitary/hypothalamic complex. Of the six chakras in the spine, the bandhas are directly associated with the active stimulation of three chakras as follows: moola bandha, mooladhara chakra; uddiyana bandha, manipura chakra; jalandhara bandha, vishuddhi chakra. Each of these physical and pranic locations is related neurologically to a specific counterpart in the spinal cord and brain, and therefore the psyche. Contraction at the

5

physical level activates and awakens hitherto dormant faculties in the brain and mind, usually present in only the most evolved mind. Mastery of the bandhas, therefore, leads to the fullest realization of our potential.

The physical, endocrinological and neurological aspects of bandhas can be understood when we appreciate the fact that the body is a complex yet well organized field of various energy systems, based on one fundamental energy principle called *prana*. Though they have vast physical repercussions of a positive nature, their main effect is on the body's energy systems at the pranic level.

According to many esoteric philosophies the downward flow of prana (*apana*) represents the part which leads man's consciousness to the lower, more earthy elements: e.g., satisfaction of instinctual desire, overindulgence, lethargy, apathy, laziness and so on. According to these philosophies, it is believed that man's essential nature is godlike and that in order to reunite or realize the 'first cause' he must redirect his consciousness. Here the role of bandhas, and especially moola bandha, is to block the descending movement of consciousness and redirect it upwards.

A useful analogy to aid our understanding of bandhas is to liken them to the locking, stopping, obstructing and redirecting power of a dam wall. Energy (physical, mental and psychic) is centralized and focused at the site of contraction so that it can be redirected for useful work as desired by the controller. These areas are infused with a fresh, vital force capable of checking imbalances in the body systems.

To further understand bandhas we must extend our view so as to see them not only as locks, but also as removers of locks or blockages, in the form of physical and mental impurities. According to the scriptures there are *granthis* or psychic knots, located at mooladhara, anahata and ajna chakras. Granthis represent blockages in man's awareness of himself at the different levels of consciousness; they obscure the true image of man's essential nature. Tradi-

6

tionally, bandhas were prescribed as one of the most effective means of untying these knots or blockages, existing as tension, anxieties, repressions and unresolved conflicts, thereby allowing us to rediscover our true nature.

The force generated from the bandhas may be likened to that of increased pressure in a tube. Imagine a piece of tubing resting vertically to the ground. This tube represents sushumna nadi (the main pranic energy channel which runs up the spine).

1. **Moola bandha** represents the sealing of the lowest portion of the tube, thus preventing the downward motion of prana. It stimulates energy in mooladhara, awakening kundalini shakti.
2. **Jalandhara bandha** seals off the top portion of the tube. Prana is now locked within this tube.
3. **Uddiyana bandha** completes maha bandha. It further increases pranic pressure by stimulating the solar plexus (manipura chakra), filling and expanding the closed tube.

Thus, when maha bandha is performed, prana is compressed in sushumna. The locks prevent its downward and upward movement at the same time stimulating energy. Release of the bandhas flushes prana through the whole body, and as prana is by nature vital, life-giving energy, the body is relaxed, toned and rejuvenated. The granthis can then be pierced and untied, expanding consciousness.

Bandhas and consciousness

According to yogic scripture, control of muscles and nerves controls the breath. Control of breath controls consciousness. Bandhas are a means of extending control over breathing and are thus a means to extend our knowledge and control over consciousness.

Breathing rate and depth is said to be affected by: states of consciousness, disease, atmospheric conditions, thoughts, exercise and emotions. Research has shown that in states of tension and fear, respiration becomes short and shallow, while in states of relaxation, people take long, deep breaths.

When bandhas are performed in conjunction with pranayama, contraction of the muscles takes place simultaneously with *kumbhaka* (internal or external breath retention). The physical lock or contraction is applied and at the same time the breath is also arrested or immobilized. As a consequence the consciousness is also arrested, stopping the flow between the polar opposites of inhalation and exhalation, birth and death, joy and sorrow, gain and loss.

Through the perfection of bandhas the yogi is able to lock himself into the 'eternal now' devoid of the dualities of existence, motion and change. His consciousness is unfettered by the modifications of thought enabling him to merge into the field of unified consciousness. As such, the bandhas induce *pratyahara* (sense withdrawal) and are preliminary techniques for meditation.

We find then that bandhas induce five different kinds of 'retention' or immobility; retention of muscles, breath, senses, thought and consciousness. Once retention of consciousness is achieved, the yogi is prepared for the next stage of his spiritual rebirth, the awakening of kundalini. The bandhas act as triggering mechanisms for the activation of this powerful force residing at the base of the spine.

Technically speaking, kundalini yoga is comprised of any technique that leads to kundalini awakening. Bandhas fall into this category and thus may be classified as techniques of kundalini and kriya yoga, as systematized by Swami Satyananda Saraswati of Bihar School of Yoga, Munger.

Of the four bandhas, we aim to focus our attention solely on moola bandha, regarded by many adepts as the most important of the bandhas. Without it, kundalini, dormant in the mooladhara chakra, will remain asleep eternally. Little has ever been written on this eminent yogic practice, depriving it of the respect and understanding which it so richly deserves.

Moola Bandha

The Sanskrit word *moola* (also written *mula*) means 'root, firmly fixed, source or cause, basis, the foot, lowest part or bottom, foundation'. *Bandha* means 'lock, restrain, shut or close'. Together the words moola and bandha refer to the contraction of *mooladhara chakra*, the seat of *kundalini*. This contraction is triggered at the 'root' of the spine or the trunk of the body, the perineum. Moola bandha is known as the 'perineal lock', contraction of the muscles around the perineal body in the male and the cervix in the female, in order to release and control energy generated by the mooladhara chakra. Moola bandha occurs simultaneously at many levels. On the physical level it is the physical contraction of muscles. However, when refined, moola bandha is the contraction of mooladhara chakra. It is important to note, therefore, that moola bandha is not just the contraction of the perineal body/cervix but also the 'locking' (contraction) of mooladhara chakra. The perineal body and cervix act as trigger points to enable us to locate the psychic centre of mooladhara chakra.

When kundalini shakti is awakened and arises from her sleep, she is the vehicle for the expansion of consciousness, enabling the individual to fully develop his innate potential and rise beyond the mundane realm of birth and death to the level of divinity.

9

The importance of moola bandha

The importance of moola bandha should not be under-estimated, for its perfection leads to a spontaneous realignment of the physical, mental and psychic bodies. The physical contraction of the perineum has the beneficial effects of: maintaining hormonal balance and stimulating and regulating the nerves that innervate the lower pelvic region, thereby regulating all the internal organs.

Moola bandha is therefore an important tool in the treatment of physical diseases of the lower abdomen e.g. digestive ailments and sexual disorders. Because the body and mind are inextricably interlinked, 'as in the body, so in the mind,' an effect on one cannot pass unnoticed by the other. Accordingly, moola bandha has the immediate effect of creating a deep sense of mental relaxation, thereby relieving most mental and psychosomatic disorders which are the direct or indirect effect of stress, tension and anxiety.

As a mental relaxant, moola bandha has been found extremely useful in the treatment of such mental disorders as depression, neurosis, some phobias, hysteria and mania. Little experimental evidence exists to substantiate the effects of moola bandha on psychosis. However, because of its effects on the brain and by virtue of the fact that moola bandha is effective in the treatment of both mania and depression, it has proved useful in correcting the extreme moods characteristic of manic-depressive psychosis, and in some cases of schizophrenia, especially in the early stages.

The effects of moola bandha on the pranic level are more pronounced than those on the physical and mental levels. It has a subtle yet powerful effect on the psychic body, acting as a trigger for the awakening of mooladhara chakra and kundalini. In so doing, moola bandha also helps to release the *brahma granthi* (psychic knot at mooladhara chakra) allowing the prana to flow up sushumna nadi. This means that moola bandha prepares one for true spiritual awakening. An aspiring sadhaka should treat moola bandha as part and parcel of his main sadhana. Though it may take time to perfect it, he will derive physical, mental and spiritual benefits far beyond his dreams or expectations.

Scriptural references

Numerous scriptural references exist that further indicate the importance of moola bandha.

In typical allegorical fashion the *Hatha Yoga Pradipika* states: "As the chief of the snakes is the support of the earth with all the mountains and forests on it, so all the tantras (yoga practices) rest on the kundalini. When the sleeping kundalini is awakened by the favour of a guru, then all the lotuses (in the six chakras or centres) and all the knots are pierced through. Sushumna nadi becomes a main road for the passage of prana. The mind itself then becomes free from all connections (with its objects of enjoyment) and death is evaded. Sushumna, shoonya padavi, brahma nadi (the innermost hollow of sushumna), mahapatha, shmashana, shambhavi, madhyamarg are names of one and the same thing.

"In order, therefore, to awaken this goddess who is sleeping at the entrance of brahma dwar (the great door), bandhas should be practised. Maha mudra, maha bandha, maha bheda, khechari, uddiyana bandha, moola bandha, jalandhara bandha, vipareeta karani, vajroli and shakti chalini. These are the ten practices which annihilate old age and death. They have been explained by Adinatha (Shiva) and give eight kinds of divine wealth. They are loved by all the siddhas (perfected ones) and are hard to attain even by the Maruts. These practices should be kept secret by every means, as one keeps a box of jewellery, and should on no account be told to anyone, just as husband and wife keep their dealings secret." (HYP, 3:1–9)

In contrast the *Gheranda Samhita*, far more direct in its approach, simply indicates that there are twenty-five techniques, the practice of which "gives success to the yogins". (GS, 3:1–3) Moola bandha is listed as one of these techniques.

11

Moola bandha is further referred to in the *Siva Samhita* where out of the many yoga practices it is listed as one of the ten best: "Now I shall tell you the best means of attaining success in yoga. The practitioners should keep it secret. It is the inaccessible yoga. When the sleeping goddess Kundalini is awakened through the grace of guru, then all the lotuses and the bonds are readily pierced through and through. Therefore, in order that the goddess who is asleep in the mouth of the brahma nadi be awakened, the bandhas should be practised with the greatest care. Out of the many practices, the following ten are the best: maha mudra, maha bandha, maha bheda, khechari, jalandhara, moola bandha, vipareeta karani, uddiyana, vajroli and shakti chalini." (SS, 4:12–15)

Regarding the techniques and benefits of moola bandha, the scriptures are equally lucid. In chapter nine of the *Hatha Yoga Pradipika*, the following is stated:

"Press the heel against the perineum and contract it firmly. Draw the apana upwards. This is known as moola bandha. (9:61)

The downward action of apana should be directed upward by the contraction of the perineum. (9:62)

Moola bandha brings about the union of prana and apana, and nada and bindu. This will bestow perfection in yoga. Of this there is no doubt. (9:64)

The apana moves upwards and when it reaches the circle of fire (manipura chakra) the flame lengthens and reaches anahata chakra. (9:65)

When the apana and the fire meet (at manipura) the prana is heated. This increases the digestive fire. (9:67)

Due to this kindling of fire, apana and prana, the sleeping kundalini is awakened; it becomes straight like a snake beaten by a stick. (9:68)

The kundalini enters the brahma nadi in the same way that a snake enters a hole. The yogi should therefore practise moola bandha daily." (9:69)

The *Gheranda Samhita* states: "Press with the heel of the left foot the region between the anus and the scrotum, and

12

contract the rectum; carefully press the intestines behind the navel on the spine; and put the right heel on the organ of generation or pubes. This is called moola bandha, destroyer of decay. The person who desires to cross the ocean of samsara, let him go to a retired place and practise this bandha in secrecy. By this practice the *vayu* (prana) is controlled undoubtedly; let one silently practise this, without laziness and with care." (GS, 3 14–17)

The *Siva Samhita* states: "Pressing well the anus with the heel, forcibly draw the *apana vayu* slowly upwards by practise. This is described as moola bandha, destroyer of decay and death. If, in the course of practise of this bandha, the yogi can unite the apana with the *prana vayu*, then it becomes *yoni mudra*. One who has accomplished yoni mudra, what can he not accomplish in this world? Sitting in padmasana posture, free from idleness, the yogi leaves the ground and moves through the air by means of this bandha. If the wise yogi is desirous of crossing the ocean of the world, let him practise this bandha in secret, in a retired place." (SS, 4:41–44)

In *Yogataravali* written by Jagatguru Adishankaracharya, moola bandha is also mentioned: "By contracting the *adhara padma* (mooladhara chakra) the fire within it is increased. If one is able at the same time to enter the apana into ida nadi, he will drink of the nectar which springs from the moon (bindu chakra) and become immortal." (Sutra 7)

Moola bandha is referred to in several of the Upanishads. According to *Yoga Tattva*, *Shandilya*, *Yoga Chudamani* and *Yoga Shikha Upanishads*, the perfection of moola bandha brings about the union of prana and apana. When they are joined together the union of nada and bindu can also take place. With this many *siddhis* (psychic abilities) are achieved. In the *Dhyanabindu* and *Shandilya Upanishads* it is also stated that he who perfects moola bandha regains his youthful vitality and is victor over old age and death.

Moola bandha is also widely mentioned in modern yogic literature. In *The Serpent Power* by Sir John Woodroffe, a recognized specialist in tantra, moola bandha is referred to:

13

"In moola bandha the perineal region (yoni) is pressed with the foot, the rectal muscle contracted (by *ashwini mudra*) and the apana drawn up. The natural course of the apana is downwards but by contraction at the mooladhara it is made to go upwards through the sushumna where it meets prana."

In *Light on Yoga*, Sri B.K.S. Iyengar, an expert in hatha yoga says that by contracting the region between the anus and the scrotum (the perineum) one performs moola bandha. "Apana vayu (the prana in the lower abdomen), whose course is downwards, is made to flow up to unite with the prana vayu, which has its seat in the region of the chest."

These ancient texts are in agreement as to the efficacy and power of moola bandha. They were written from personal experience, and have served as the foundation for the myriad schools of tantra and yoga now in existence. Their testimony has been further backed up by countless generations of aspiring *sadhakas* who have proven for themselves what they saw written in the texts. You too can have this experience if you are diligent, steadfast and determined.

Anatomical and Physiological Aspects

Much confusion surrounds the correct way to perform moola bandha, which muscles are involved and where they are located. In translating the original Sanskrit texts many commentators, being unfamiliar with yogic practices or not fully conversant with the basic anatomical aspects of the pelvic floor, have unknowingly led people to believe that there are *two* ways to practise moola bandha when, in fact, there is only *one*.

Many translations of hatha yoga texts describe moola bandha as pressing the heel against the perineum and contracting the anus. It should be carefully noted, however, that this practice is *ashwini mudra*. The ancient tantric texts (the scriptural foundation of kundalini yoga and kriya yoga) reveal that moola bandha is performed by relaxing the anus (sphincter muscles) and contracting only the perineal body.

As the scriptures did not clearly differentiate anatomically between the sexes, some confusion has arisen over how moola bandha should be practised by males and females, owing to anatomical differences. Scriptural descriptions all relate to the male body. In the male the heel is placed against the perineum behind the scrotum and in front of the anus. In the female it is also placed in the perineum, pressed against the outer vagina.

The perineum is a group of muscles which extends the entire length of the pelvic floor, related to both the urogenital

15

and anal areas. It is not a single muscle. Moola bandha is not contraction of the whole perineum as this contraction will bring about moola bandha as well as vajroli mudra and ashwini mudra. The actual point of physical contraction varies according to sex. In the male it is the perineal body while in the female it is the area around the cervix. When the average person contracts the anal sphincters the perineum is also involuntarily contracted. Because contraction of the perineum is difficult for the beginner, the first exponents of hatha yoga, realizing the interconnection between the anal sphincters and the perineum, recommended contraction of the anal muscles (ashwini mudra) thereby leading to an involuntary contraction of the perineum. Personal experience, however, will verify that the direct (conscious) contraction of the perineum has a distinct effect on the physical and mental bodies, different from that of the indirect method of contracting the anus. Contraction of the anus is a necessary preparation for the more subtle and difficult practice of moola bandha.

Perineum and perineal body
It is indeed important to have a clear picture in your mind of the basic muscle structure of the lower pelvis or perineum, not only in order to practise moola bandha correctly, but also in order to understand the anatomical interrelationships between moola bandha with ashwini and vajroli mudras, two techniques also performed in the area of the lower pelvis.

The perineum overlies the outlet of the pelvis. Its internal boundaries are in front of the pubic arch (the bone slightly above the genitalia) and behind the tip of the coccyx (tail bone). Its external boundaries are the scrotum/clitoris and the buttocks.

The muscles of the perineum are divided into two groups:
1. Those of the anal region -- found at the end of the gastrointestinal tract.
2. Those of the urogenital region – around the urinary and sexual organs.

The muscles of the anal region, the larger of the two groups, and the muscles of the urogenital group are connected by fibrous tissue and are interrelated to the extent that movement of one group usually elicits a response from the other. Thus, controlled movement of one area alone requires considerable skill. The muscles of the perineum are normally utilized only on the occasions of urination, defecation and ejaculation/orgasm.

We have not been taught to consciously isolate pelvic muscle groups with the same exactness as we have the muscles of the arms and legs, which we use continually in specialized, conscious daily activity. The reason why most people find precise nervous control over the perineum more difficult than that of the arms and legs may be due to the fact that the areas in the brain associated with the motor activities of the perineum are small when compared with the larger, more developed areas regulating the arms, hands and face, allowing finer movements and better control. By regular practise of moola bandha the area in the brain associated with the perineum will develop so that one may gain complete control over such processes as urination, defecation and sexual intercourse. The pelvic muscles are mainly required for all subconscious and unconscious autonomic activity. This lack of conscious nervous control makes it difficult for a person to both urinate and defecate at the same time.

The implication of this for the yoga beginner is that the contraction of one set of perineal muscles involves the involuntary contraction of the other. We can better understand this when we remember that the third and fourth toes are joined by fibrous tissue and it is extremely difficult without practise to move one without moving the other. Because of the interconnection of muscles and other fibrous tissue and lack of precise control over the nerves in the perineum, it is difficult to perform vajroli or ashwini mudras without performing moola bandha at the same time. This applies equally to men and women.

17

It is necessary to fully appreciate the fact that the perineum is not one muscle but a group of muscles which are common to both sexes. Likewise, there exists a clear distinction between the perineum and the perineal body or central tendon of the perineum. In the male and female the perineal body is a small fibromuscular node about one to one and a half inches in front of the anus and approximately two inches inside the body. Towards this point the pelvic muscles converge and are attached: the superficial and deep transverse perineal muscles, bulbospongiosus, the external anal sphincter and the levator ani. The rectum also sends some of its muscle fibres to this central and vitally important structure, which divides the urogenital area from the anal region.

It is a compact complete node, and its importance to the pelvic floor in the female is such that if damaged or torn, as in pregnancy for example, it may cause the uterus, ovaries and/or rectum to prolapse (slip out of place). Therefore the perineal body, especially in the female body, plays a very important role and is the pivot around which everything is joined or supported.

In the male, the perineal body is the trigger point for mooladhara chakra. In the female, however, the back of the neck of the womb or cervix, rather than the perineal body, is the trigger for mooladhara chakra.

Anatomical aspects refined

Having discussed the perineum and the perineal body, we can now explore in finer anatomical detail the distinguishing areas of the three different yoga practices that are performed in the region of the pelvic floor: vajroli mudra, ashwini mudra and moola bandha.

The muscles contracted in these three practices are:

• **Ashwini mudra**: The anal area including the following muscles: sphincter ani externus and levator ani which consists of the pubococcygeus, iliococcygeus and puborectalis, i.e. the anal muscles are contracted.

18

- **Moola bandha**: The area between the anus and scrotum/ clitoris, the perineal body/cervix is contracted.
- **Vajroli mudra**: The urogenital muscles including the transversi perinei superficialis, ischiocavernosus, bulbospongiosus, transversus perinei profundus and the sphincter urethrae, are contracted. In the male the penis is slightly contracted inwards; in the female, the clitoris, lower vaginal muscles and the urethra are contracted.

The actual location of these muscles can best be described by personal experience. Whenever you have to consciously withhold the onset of urination or defecation you become acutely aware of the muscles necessary for both vajroli mudra (preventing urination) and ashwini mudra (preventing defecation). It is difficult to release both these muscle groups at the same time (though structurally it is possible). Once, however, either of these muscle groups is relaxed (urogenital is usually the first), the excretory process may take place. When excretion has concluded, both vajroli and/or ashwini again spontaneously occur for a short time.

Moola bandha: men and women

Embryologically the penis and vagina are formed from the same structure while still in the foetus. When hormonal activity begins, the basic genital structure forms according to the sex of the foetus which has already been determined at conception.

Thus, despite the different formation of sexual organs, the basic muscle structure of the lower pelvic region is the same for male and female and the vagina occupies approximately the same area as the root of the penis. The neurological and hormonal connections with this area are likewise the same for both sexes.

Conclusion

In the beginning the student will find difficulty in asserting conscious control over the perineal area as the brain is not tuned to such fine muscular manipulation in this area. The

19

practice of moola bandha reactivates the areas in the brain controlling this lower region of the body, bringing the neuronal circuits responsible for its control into the sphere of consciousness.

This growth process takes time and in the meantime, while practising moola bandha, it is important not to become frustrated if you cannot contract the perineal body or the cervix without contracting the anus or genital organs also. In the initial stages of practice this is to be expected. Be assured that control will definitely come with time, practice and perseverance.

Neurological and Endocrinological Aspects

Though moola bandha seems to be concerned with events occurring at the southern pole of the body, it is a means of directly manipulating and influencing the brain and its neurological and endocrinological function at the northern-most extremity. In this way, moola bandha influences our behaviour, personality and mental state by exerting a positive and coordinating effect on the whole physical body via the brain. Moola bandha helps to integrate the neurological and endocrinological function of the body by manipulation of body energies.

Neurone cells are the basic units of the nervous system. Their function is to conduct energy impulses which transmit information. Varying in size and shape, there are more than twelve billion neurones in the body that go to make up the nervous system and play an important role in the shaping of consciousness, distributing the energies of the body. In this way the different body organs are controlled; turned on or off, sped up or slowed down, given fine tuning and coordinated. The nervous system is coordinated with the endocrine system by way of a central mid brain structure, the limbic system. Within this lies the hypothalamus which controls the autonomic component of the nervous system as well as the endocrine glands.

The nervous system allows for fine, precise, immediate control of the body with very little delay. The endocrine

21

system, on the other hand, is a slower controlling mechanism, regulating the metabolism and basic structure and function. In the normal individual both these systems are coordinated and harmonized within themselves and with each other so that all bodily processes function at an optimal level, no system trying to outdo any other. Each cell in the body works to maintain the health and integrity of every other cell, organ and structure.

The nervous system

The nervous system is divided into the following components:

- **Central nervous system**: This is an organization of two principal components, the spinal cord and the brain. The spinal cord serves as a conduction path to and from the brain which regulates the complex activities of the body and mind. It is a highly developed computer which integrates whole body function in terms of sensation, movement, thought, feeling, intellectual faculties, and higher intuitive processes.
- **Peripheral nervous system**: This is comprised of those neurones which lie outside the bony case formed by the skull and spine, and includes autonomic and sensory/motor nervous systems. Motor nerves take messages from the brain to the different parts of the body and sensory nerves bring messages back.
- **Autonomic nervous system**: This regulates all automatic body functions including heart rate, blood pressure, endocrine and digestive processes, and so on. Although not normally under our conscious control, they can become so through the techniques of biofeedback and yoga. The sympathetic aspect of the autonomic nervous system generally comes into play when we experience stress, tension or strong emotions. The system tends to be active when we are calm and relaxed.

With the practice of moola bandha we see an elaborate interplay of the different aspects of the nervous system. The initial impetus to perform moola bandha stimulates the

22

cerebral cortex of the central nervous system. The message to contract the perineum is relayed to the second, third and fourth sacral (peripheral) nerves through the spine. Having accepted the nervous stimulus, the sacral nerves proceed to contract the perineum (peripheral nervous system). The contraction completed, the effects on the autonomic nervous system may now come into play.

Parasympathetic fibres concerned with relaxation emerge only from the neck (cervical) and sacral (pelvic) areas of the spinal cord. Thus, with the stimulation of the sacral nerves not only has the perineum successfully been contracted but also the parasympathetic nervous system is now dominant over the sympathetic nervous system, resulting in a deep sense of rest and relaxation in body and mind. The autonomic nervous system maintains constant tone and monitors any change in the body's internal environment. With the performance of moola bandha the whole internal environment is altered, the blood pressure decreases, as do the respiration and heart rate, and so on. The sensations of relaxation and pleasure generated by this practice are relayed back to the brain (via the peripheral nervous system) where they are analyzed by the higher mental faculties of the cerebral cortex, and transmitted to the mind for conscious appreciation and enjoyment.

A similar neurological process occurs in the practices of ashwini and vajroli mudras, the difference being that the initial mental impulse responsible for the contraction of the various muscles is generated from a different area of the brain's cortex, or outer layer. The nature of nervous control over these muscles basically remains the same.

It is important to realize that there is a difference between the unconscious, involuntary processes involved in urination and defecation, and conscious contraction as experienced in yogic practice. In the first case, the neuronal circuits related to the perineal area are usually outside the normal range of conscious awareness. Through moola bandha we can learn to use those same neuronal circuits as part of an

23

act of will, within the range of conscious awareness, thereby enabling us to:

- Precisely control all physical activity in this area, projecting our control into deeper pranic or psychic areas.
- Be consciously aware of the processes of the perineal area and arrest any disharmony before disease manifests e.g. piles, constipation, prostatic hypertrophy.
- Retrain the brain to disentangle confused or crossed circuits so that the sensory motor system is coordinated, and health of the whole body maintained.
- Have greater conscious control.

These effects have ramifications for all the other components of the body.

The nerve which supplies the perineum is the pudendal nerve. It derives its fibres from the second, third and fourth sacral nerves, which in turn originate from the sacral plexus in the lower back. This nerve sends branches to the vagina, clitoris, penis, scrotum, rectum, anus and perineal muscles and is both sensory and motor in function. The interaction of the nerves in the perineum with the brain and the rest of the body is extremely intricate. The nervous system is delicate and sophisticated, but our precise control over this instrument is often left wanting. Yet despite all its networks, myriads of pathways and connections, it is possible to unravel its mysteries and regain conscious control of the total organism. The technique of moola bandha is a way to that goal and the catch-word is 'practice'.

Damage to either nerves, spinal cord or brain may seriously impede, or render impossible, control over muscles in the body. In cases where people have had no voluntary control over the muscles of the pelvic floor, it was impossible for them to contract any of the muscles or muscle groups of the perineum. Closer investigation revealed that in most cases some damage had been incurred by the nervous system.

Similarly, the opposite phenomenon has also occurred. Namely, after the contraction of specified muscles the practitioner has failed to be able to let them go and relax.

The brain fires off a train of continuous impulses which send the muscles into spasm, leading to unpleasant subjective physical and mental sensations. From our experience this is caused by a psycho-physical inability to properly control the contraction and release of muscles, coupled with an excessive discharge of pranic energy which the body has not yet been accustomed to handle. As a result the circuits overload. These phenomena require expert assistance and guidance.

Though such experiences are rare, the implications for the students are obvious. Any break in the complex links between the muscles and the brain will have definite repercussions on the total system. Thus, sound health is a vital requisite for the practice of moola bandha. The preparatory techniques must also be fully mastered. Moola bandha must not be overpractised in the beginning and the guidance of an expert teacher must always be on hand.

The endocrine system
The endocrine system is a body control system which is comprised of glands secreting powerful hormones into the blood stream. The endocrine glands are not only responsible for metabolic processes and the control of all biological activity in the body, but also hormonal balance profoundly affects our personality and character. There are eight endocrine glands in the body: pituitary, pineal, thyroid, parathyroid, thymus, adrenals, pancreas and gonads.

The endocrine system is self-regulating in that hormone secretions from any gland is activated in part by other hormones in the bloodstream. All information feeds back to the master controlling gland, the pituitary. Thus, the endocrine glands are all interrelated, interlinked and interdependent. One diseased or malfunctioning endocrine gland will impair the efficient functioning of the others and will, at the same time, have direct or indirect bearing on the total wellbeing of the body, through its effect on the brain.

On a more subtle level, each of the endocrine glands is related to one of the chakras. There is, however, no

25

endocrine gland specifically related to mooladhara chakra, though according to yogic philosophy, the perineal body is the vestige of a gland which has atrophied in the course of evolution. The practice of moola bandha reactivates this vestige, which has very subtle effects on the brain and the pituitary/pineal/hypothalamic complex. At the same time it stimulates the gonads in both sexes, as it is intimately related to this system. This stimulation turns on the energy in the whole pelvic area, making it available for other body processes. In yogic terminology, the energy is called *ojas* and can be channelled by various techniques such as vajroli mudra, for productive and useful work in the body and mind. Moola bandha may lead to increased sexual energy; it should not, however, lead to ejaculation. The practice of vajroli mudra is therefore learned after moola bandha to prevent this dissipation of sexual (pranic) energy and encourages its sublimation for a higher purpose – the reanimation of the latent capacities in the brain.

Thus, moola bandha allows us to gain control over the endocrine system as well as energizing body and mind. This is because endocrine glands (at the physical level) correspond to the chakras, whirling vortices of energy (at the pranic level). Moola bandha stimulates mooladhara and swadhisthana chakras, sending energy through the body, invigorating us and making our personality positive and dynamic.

The neuro-endocrine axis

With the energy gained through control of the endocrine glands, we can act with determination and spontaneous creativity. Through moola bandha, combined with other yogic disciplines, we learn to channel the nervous energy at will so that we can act in a more graceful, flowing way, able to perform more difficult tasks with greater dexterity. When the brain becomes ordered and more synchronized, we function better at all levels with increased understanding and willpower, and are able to accomplish more in our life with attendant satisfaction and gain.

Pranic Effects

Moola bandha has an immensely powerful effect on the nervous system and endocrine glands, however, its main effect is on the energy systems of the body, those of the pranas and chakras. Moola bandha is a pranic technique more than a physical one. It requires us to take our whole awareness to the mooladhara chakra in the perineum where we focus and concentrate our energies in the attempt to contract a hitherto unknown and hidden area of the body that we have never isolated and contracted before. Therefore, it is a more subtle technique than uddiyana or jalandhara bandha, though all bandhas deal directly with the pranic energies of the body.

Though it appears to be a simple muscular contraction, the real work is psychic. As the energies are stimulated there, we become more conscious of the area. We become aware of the chakra and the psychic components, nadis, etc. In time and with persistent practice we can refine our energy and convert it into a highly concentrated force, just as a laser can convert the energy from a ten watt bulb into a light source which concentrates energy over a one inch surface more intense than the surface of the sun. When pranic energy in mooladhara chakra has thus been refined, the dormant potential energy is released. The process builds on itself, snowballing into a virtuous circle of ever-increasing health, awareness and bliss.

27

Prana is the omnipresent vital energy of the cosmos, the life force within man and the whole material universe. In man's physical body, prana is said to be of two forms, physical and mental energy. It flows in the pranic body in *nadis*, currents or channels of force. Of the 72,000 nadis in the pranic body, three are most important: ida, pingala and sushumna. Ida represents mental energy, pingala physical energy and sushumna the unification of the mental and the physical aspects. Running along the sushumna nadi are chakras which act as transformers, channelling prana into the body via the nerve plexus and endocrine glands, positioned along the spinal axis from the brain to the pelvic floor.

In the tantras it is written that all of the 72,000 nadis in the body originate from the *medhra* (foundation, base) in the *sukshma sharira* (astral body) located just above mooladhara. This *medhra* is the triangular shaped seat of life in the astral body related to those nerves called the *cauda equina* (horse's tail) in the physical body – the nerve bundle which comes out from the spine at about the level of the hips and travels down to the end of the spine and perineal body.

The full impact of moola bandha is now exposed by the fact that not only is the perineal body/cervix contracted, but all of the 72,000 nadis, for which it is the source, are also stimulated. Similarly, as all the nadis are linked to the mechanisms of the central nervous system, the practice of moola bandha also represents a contraction of certain switches in the brain, which stimulate physical, mental and spiritual relaxation. Also, hitherto dormant areas of the brain (an estimated 90%) begin to plug into conscious awareness, increasing our ability to live life fully. When prana is increased, more and more of the brain is available for our conscious control.

Subdivisions of prana
According to yogic philosophy there are twelve subpranas of mahaprana in the human body, the five major pranas being: *prana, apana, samana, udana* and *vyana*. These pranas

are not essentially different from one another. Although they operate at different frequencies, they are different aspects of the one unifying, life-sustaining, cosmic energy. Just as the various colours of the rainbow complement each other to form white light, so the twelve pranas functionally complement one another to create harmony within the body. Of the divisions of *mahaprana* (cosmic energy) apana is the downward moving force below the navel responsible for defecation, urination, labour and so on. Prana resides in the chest and moves with the breath.

The performance of moola bandha has a considerable effect on pranic flow, particularly the flow of apana. In *The Serpent Power* Sir John Woodroffe writes about this apanic flow: "The natural course of the apana is downward, but by contraction at mooladhara it is made to go upward through the sushumna where it meets prana. When the latter vayu reaches the region of fire below the navel, the fire becomes bright and strong, being fanned by apana. The heat in the body then becomes very powerful, and kundalini, feeling it, awakes from her sleep."

Compare the above to what is said in the *Siva Samhita:* "Pressing well the perineum with the heel, forcibly draw the apana vayu upwards slowly by practise." (SS, 4:41–44)

In the *Hatha Yoga Pradipika* there is also reference to the effect of moola bandha on pranic flow, as quoted previously, (pp.14,15). The perfection of moola bandha brings about a union of prana and apana in manipura chakra. With this the sleeping kundalini is awakened and sushumna is energized.

Moola bandha and pranayama

For maximum benefits moola bandha should be practised in conjunction with pranayama. This is because while pranayama stimulates and allows us control of the flow of prana, the bandha directs it to required areas, thus preventing dissipation. In the context of pranayama, apana moves up with inhalation (*pooraka*) and prana moves down with exhalation (*rechaka*), while a balance between inhalation and exhalation signifies the retention of breath (*kumbhaka*) which occurs spontaneously when prana and apana unite.

Moola bandha is utilized with kumbhaka as it helps to turn the apana upwards. In the beginning moola bandha should be practised with *antar kumbhaka* (internal breath retention). Simultaneously the region of the perineum is contracted and pulled up towards the diaphragm. When the practitioner can perform moola bandha while holding the breath inside, without the slightest strain or discomfort, then he should attempt the more difficult practice of moola bandha with *bahir kumbhaka* (external breath retention) which has a more powerful effect.

The *Hatha Yoga Pradipika* states that kumbhaka is of two kinds – *sahit kumbhaka* (borne, endured, supported by willpower, produced by conscious effort) and *kevala kumbhaka* (spontaneous, absolute, highest possible). Sahit kumbhaka should be practised until one achieves mastery over pranayama, when we achieve kevala kumbhaka. The essential difference between these forms is that sahit is 'the way' and kevala is 'the end'. Kevala kumbhaka occurs automatically when kundalini enters the sushumna, but takes place only after mooladhara chakra has been fully awakened. Kevala has many names: *vidya* (knowledge), *samvit* (pure consciousness) and *turiya* (beyond the three dimensions of consciousness). It is the highest experience of yoga, the end goal.

One should not confuse kevala kumbhaka with the simple kumbhaka that occurs during the beginning stages of meditation when the breath seems to stop. Many yoga students, while in meditation, will have experienced for themselves the breath becoming slower. It is not uncommon that as the breath becomes no more than a mild flicker, many students are overcome by a sense of fear and un-certainty and discontinue the practice. Some people may also become extremely frightened and think, 'If I stop breathing altogether surely I will die'. Experience will show that this is not the case but that rather, once the barrier of the breath is overcome, one is transported into divine realms.

If you have met with this fear, rest assured that the experience is only the suspension of the breath, *not* the actual stopping of the breath. This is the springboard into your own inner consciousness, but if the fear is not overcome by a strong will and unconquerable faith, you will find that the moment you experience fear, the breathing pattern will become increasingly more rapid, leading your consciousness back to extroversion and the meditation is lost. This suspension of breath (kumbhaka) plays a definite role in the perfection of moola bandha. Only when the mind is completely concentrated will the breath cease, and moola bandha is a powerful means to concentrate the mind and energy. When combined with breath control and awareness it is an even more powerful means to attain kevala kumbhaka.

Moola bandha can be performed in conjunction with nadi shodhana pranayama, for example. In this way the maximum benefits of moola bandha can be derived, and at the same time acute sensitivity toward inhalation (apana/pooraka), exhalation (prana/rechaka), and breath retention (antar/bahir kumbhaka) is developed. From this control, awareness is developed and prana can then be consciously directed. As mooladhara chakra is the storehouse of prana, and moola bandha the key to release it, control is essential.

Once control over the practice has been achieved, we can begin to slowly awaken mooladhara chakra and the kundalini shakti which lies within it. Then we may enjoy the bliss which arises from the union of prana and apana, nada and bindu, the union of the formed with the formless.

Moola Therapy

Moola bandha has a twofold role in the treatment of disease at both a therapeutic and preventive practice. At the therapeutic level it allows us to regain a state of health on the physical, emotional and mental planes, while at the preventive level it allows us to maintain health and expand our normal, stable function to the cosmic level where we can do, and enjoy, so much more. By this subtle yet powerful practice, we gain control over many of the neural, pranic and psychic faculties which we have not been able to consciously utilize due to ignorance of their existence.

Moola bandha is an energy charging practice with great specific benefit for many diseases of mental and pranic origin, where there is depression of physical energy, imbalance in the pranic body or imbalance of the mental body. It should not be used therapeutically in high energy diseases of the physical body such as high blood pressure, vertigo, high intracranial pressure, amenorrhoea.

At the physical level, it is directly effective in such diseases as: piles, constipation, anal fissures, ulcers, prostatitis, some cases of prostatic hypertrophy, and chronic pelvic infections. Because it releases energy, it is also effective in other illnesses especially psychosomatic and some degenerative illnesses. Its effect spreads throughout the body via the brain and endocrine systems, making it very beneficial in cases of asthma, bronchitis, arthritis, and so on. All these problems should be handled under the expert guidance of an experienced teacher, guru, or healer who will combine moola bandha with other practices such as asanas, pranayama, kundalini kriyas, bandhas, mudras, and so on. The amount of practice will obviously vary from case to case, and should be coupled with an adequate diet, a positive attitude, and willingness to forfeit certain behaviour patterns directly attributed to the cause of the complaint.

We have experienced that moola bandha is most effective when applied to sexual and psychological problems.

Sexual aspects
Moola bandha is both a means to sexual control, brahmacharya, and to alleviate a multitude of sexual problems. This apparently contradictory statement has created a great deal of debate, concern and confusion, most people fearing that through the practice of moola bandha they will become impotent or celibate. From both the scientific and spiritual view, moola bandha does not cause loss of sexual virility, rather, it allows one to direct sexual energy either upward for spiritual development, or downward to enhance marital relations. In this way we remove guilt, frustration and suppression of sexual energy, associated with misdirection of the life force that leads on to psychological disease, neurosis and psychosomatic degeneration.

The psychic energy of the body can be expressed or manifested in different ways, including both spiritual and sexual expression. The notion of expressing energy is a basic teaching of yoga, particularly kundalini yoga.

In the words of Dr Jack Lee Rosenberg, author of *Total Orgasm*: "Spirituality and orgasm are different expressions of the same life force. There is a great similarity between an intense religious experience and a total orgasm. Each is often called a 'peak experience'... a feeling of being at one with the universe for a brief moment. In orgasm, the experience of being swept out of the ego or mind is not uncommon. The giving of oneself to another with love, total

33

surrender, loss of duality and merger describes the religious experience as well as it describes sexual union."

Moola bandha increases vitality. For this reason it is extremely useful in treatment of many sexual problems of an inhibitory nature such as impotence, fear of sexual expression and underperformance, and so on. The successful practice of moola bandha in these cases re-establishes normal, healthy sexual relations, thereby enhancing or recreating harmony in the total marital relationship.

Moola bandha also increases sexual retentive power. The implications of this further magnify the possibility of retrieving the threads of a marital relationship threatened with extinction by the sexual dissatisfaction of one or both of its partners. With an increase in sexual retentiveness, sexual relations become more satisfying and fulfilling. Utilizing further tantric practices with awareness, breath control and spiritual appreciation of the divinity residing in one's partner, it is also possible to further enhance the sexual act. Through the practice of moola bandha, sexual relationships will tend to be more enjoyable and spiritually more meaningful. For, by realizing the true nature of the primal energy residing in mooladhara, your sexual partner becomes as one of the gods and the sexual act a symbolic expression of the union of Shiva (male, consciousness) and Shakti (female, energy).

Both the householder and the renunciate are striving for this mystical union but where the householder achieves union through the framework of marriage, the renunciate sublimates outward sexual expression to achieve inner union. The paths vary for not everyone is suited to the same kind of lifestyle. However, the goal is the same: the transcendental union of consciousness and energy.

Medical benefits

Female: Moola bandha may be used to alleviate dysmenorrhoea (painful menstruation); however, if you have amenorrhoea (absence of period) refrain from the practice of moola bandha until you have sought the expert guidance of a doctor and yoga teacher who will assess the cause.

Moola bandha has also proved useful in childbirth. A pregnant woman may continue to practise moola bandha along with certain other yogic practices right up to the time of labour in order to maintain elasticity in the vaginal muscles, aiding in painless delivery. It is also suggested that women should practise moola bandha, ashwini and vajroli mudras, and other yoga practices, immediately after childbirth as this will assist in retoning muscles stretched during pregnancy. Moola bandha is also excellent for treating prolapse, leucorrhoea and urinary (stress) incontinence.

Male: Moola bandha alleviates spermatthorea (leakage of semen), helps prevent inguinal hernia, and controls testosterone secretion and sperm formation; pacifies passions, which influences coronary behaviour.

Scientific research has shown that the problems associated with menopause are closely correlated with one's mental and emotional state. Men and women who are cheerful, healthy, and have a positive outlook on life pass through menopause with little or no difficulty. However because the physical effects are more evident in women, a larger percentage may tend to become pessimistic, depressed, worried and anxious, and have a great deal of trouble accepting and handling menopause. The practice of moola bandha allows for a smooth metamorphosis at this time by rebalancing hormonal changes, preventing such unpleasant symptoms as lethargy, irritability, depression, high blood pressure and giddiness. Contrary to numerous superstitions and myths, people do not lose their sexuality at menopause, rather their capacity for sexual expression continues into old age. Thus moola bandha will ensure continuity of a healthy, fulfilling life and may be performed from two different points of view as follows:

1. For the householder, in order to solve sexual problems and enhance, maintain and sustain a healthy sexual relationship.

35

2. For the renunciate, to sublimate the energy of overt sexual expression into the awakening of higher centres.

In both cases, constant awareness of the spirituality inherent in sexual energy can be maintained, transforming the sensual act into spiritual union. It is possible that through the practice of moola bandha immense sexual energy will be generated. Then this energy must find a positive means of expression; the sadhaka begins to perform vajroli mudra so that it may be rechannelled upwards into the sushumna. Others find an expression for this energy through working, painting, writing, inventing, and so on. Whatever the avenue of expression, this vital energy or ojas should not be lost or wasted in idle sensual enjoyment. Ultimately, ojas is the majestic unfoldment of the most highly refined consciousness. Whether it reaches its final culmination in the sahasrara or remains bound by the walls of mooladhara is a decision that exemplifies a turning point to spiritual life.

Psychotherapeutic value
Moola bandha, and bandhas in general, are a powerful means of relaxing the body and mind. They relax the mental tenseness that we see mirrored in various personalities as phobia, mania, hysteria, depression, and anxiety. Even schizophrenia and other psychoses are amenable to moola therapy if they are caught in their early stages and the personality has been previously stable. This is because moola bandha is a mental purgative, releasing the subconscious and unconscious mind of suppressed anxieties and hidden mental blocks beyond the consciousness, yet causing difficulties in life.

If the body is healthy, moola bandha increases the activity of the parasympathetic nervous system, lowering the breathing rate, heart rate, blood pressure and stabilizing the brain waves. The whole endocrine system is rebalanced which leads to stabilization and equilibrium of the personality. As a result of this the mind starts to feel relaxed and healthy. We come in touch with the body and learn how to control it. The mind is a wondrous and amazing thing but few of us have realized its infinite capacity. Moola bandha, even though to the uninitiated it may seem no more than simple physical muscle contraction, is one means of raising our normal consciousness and fulfilling its enormous potential by the arousal of kundalini shakti.

The psychophysical relationship

Moola bandha capitalizes on the mind-body link. We might wonder how it is that contraction of such a small area of the physical body can have such powerful effects on the whole human organism. Yogic philosophy states that the effects of moola bandha are more powerful than contraction of all the other muscles of the body combined. To better understand this we can turn to modern western psychological theory.

Forty years ago, the American psychologist Edward Jacobson pioneered the first major work into the area of relaxation. He gathered evidence to show that through relaxation certain changes in the autonomic nervous system were facilitated, e.g. blood pressure and heart rate decreases, the breathing pattern becomes more regular and stable, and the level of adrenaline released into the bloodstream decreases. This research was conducted in passive relaxation techniques. As interest grew and the experimental procedures became more elaborate, it became apparent that the physiological changes due to relaxation were associated with certain psychological states, such as: calmness, optimism, positiveness, peace of mind and also increased concentration.

Further physiological research realized the important fact that mental tension and anxiety are absorbed into the muscle structure of the body in the form of spasm or rigidity. With this realization, orthodox passive techniques moved in a new direction known as 'dynamic relaxation'.

Attention was directed towards the muscles, and various methods, including massage techniques, were devised to alleviate muscle rigidity. The most effective method, and the one still most commonly used today, was incorporated into what is called muscle relaxation therapy. In this therapy the subject is not a passive recipient but an active (dynamic) participant. This technique showed that the most efficient way to release muscle spasm was to first exaggerate the tension in muscle groups by powerfully contracting the muscles to the limit and then slowly releasing the contraction. By this, not only did the patient experience the feeling of 'letting go' but he also became consciously aware of tension spots that previously (sometimes for months and years) went unnoticed.

Moola bandha is performed in much the same way as the method already outlined for muscle relaxation therapy and its effects runs directly parallel. That is, several of the muscles connected to the perineal body are contracted and held for some duration, and then released. Inherent in this process is the release of physical and mental tensions.

The psychoemotional relationship

The view of moola bandha as relaxation therapy is only a partial one, however, for moola bandha, as we have already seen, it is not a primarily physical practice. The physical contraction is merely a means to locate a psychic body component. Then the real work starts. The unconscious mind is stimulated so that suppressed mental energy is allowed to surface into conscious awareness where we can deal with it through various yogic practices such as antar mouna, relaxed witnessing of inner experiences, with the element of control.

This release of emotional energy is called abreaction in modern psychological terminology and was a technique propagated by Freud, Bruer, Brown and others. Freud had discovered that remembering past dramas and memories was useless in the psychotherapeutic process unless emotional energy was released at the same time. This requires one to consciously relive this experience, thereby freeing one from dissipated, and functional non-disintegrated energy that creates pain and suffering.

Abreaction encourages the patient to emotionally relive or 'abreact' the terrifying or anxiety-provoking experiences which had led to psychological disturbance and even breakdown. In the medical setting he was drugged in order to break down inhibitions, then suggestions were made to him that he was in the original situation of terror and stress. If the abreaction was successful, the effect was to stir up tense excitement in the nervous system which often produced violent outbursts of emotion such as tears, anger, aggression, fear, and laughter.

Moola bandha is nowhere near as violent a technique as drug abreaction, but it works on the same line at a more subtle level. The relaxation of tension in the body allows suppressed energies to be released, bringing with them the conflicts and neuroses from the subconscious and unconscious depths, purifying body and mind. As a result we may experience strange emotions, feelings and thoughts because of the practice, but these should be kept within perspective and realized to be manifestations of the cleansing process.

When the release of energy occurs through moola bandha, unconscious desires, anxieties and tensions surface. When this happens, the person, according to abreactive therapy, is encouraged to release the tension both emotionally and overtly. However, according to yoga, the release occurs through the practice of antar mouna – acting as a detached witness to all thoughts and emotion. Through mental and emotional arousal the mind is purged of unwanted stress and anxiety and we feel cleansed, freed, revitalized. Some people may want to cry, and this is a valid means of release to be encouraged by the yoga teacher. Others may laugh, overjoyed that their minds are becoming so light and free. Still others will watch the process with detached equanimity, neither crying nor laughing but just being aware. All these ways release poisonous emotional energies which have created neurotic mental and neuronal mechanisms.

When learning moola bandha we proceed slowly, for if we jump into the practice without first learning detached awareness and becoming used to the release of emotional energy, we may be caught unaware, and thus be overcome by the results of the practice. The *Hatha Yoga Pradipika* indicates that the unconscious complexes have the capacity to become as powerful as a 'sleeping snake struck by a stick'. Through slow progress and expert guidance, this will not happen. If it does, then appropriate techniques and measures can be utilized to redirect energy outwards. An experienced teacher is necessary for this.

If we imagine that our neuroses are fixed patterns of brain neurones and mental mechanisms which force us to react in predetermined ways, and therefore inappropriately to our environment, we can see how they destroy our lives. Usually the energy of these neuronal and mental circuits are outside the field of our awareness. Moola bandha and other energy-releasing techniques such as kunjal send the pranic energy directly to the brain and mind, increasing our circle of awareness, which naturally starts to include within it recognition of our neurotic patterns.

As soon as we start to become aware of ourselves, we can begin to change for the better. As a result of the elimination of mental and emotional problems, increased sensitivity is developed to one's own internal and emotional environment. It is further heightened through practising awareness. As sensitivity and awareness both expand, one's internal vision is expanded, and in this way our mental problems can be solved as we can see the source or roots of the problems. Thus moola bandha is a means to cut the mental problems at the roots and so establish mental health and wellbeing.

Breaking through the barriers

Moola bandha offers an infinitely powerful technique capable of breaking down the rigid barriers that have been built up in the mind over the years, thereby expelling deep unconscious conflicts and complexes that are not easily accessible to modern psychological techniques. This is because of moola bandha's action on mooladhara chakra, and the pranas of the body. Psychiatry on the other hand relies on drugs and other physical processes, or psychotherapy, which cannot get into the depths of the mind.

Even abreaction therapy could not help some people, such as severe depressives too inhibited to release the required amount of emotion to break up the depressive condition. Perhaps this was because these more severe and long-term conditions had become cemented into the body and mind and thus were no longer amenable to abreaction, because abreaction only allows free unconscious material to rise and be expelled, not concentrating on the physical aspects of anxiety.

Wilhelm Reich's work with repressed sexual energy exemplifies the above concepts. He formulated the concept of 'character armour' or muscle tension and posture rigidity which he says makes itself felt as 'character resistance' (instinctual desires and defensive functions of the ego).

Character armour, for Reich, represented layers of defence mechanisms which had been psychosomatically transferred into the physical body and could be pictorially schematized similar to geological or archaeological stratification. As such it represented the 'solidified history, of the patient, the deeper tensions being the oldest. Reich states that conflicts which have been active at a certain period of life always leave their traces in the character, in the form of physical and mental rigidity. Each conflict forms a layer in the individual's character. Each of these layers in the character structure is a piece of life history which is preserved in another form, that is, physically, and is still active. He demonstrated that by loosening up these layers, the old conflicts could – more or less easily – be revived. If the layers were particularly numerous and functioning automatically, if they formed a compact unit which was difficult to penetrate, they seemed like an 'armour' surrounding the living organism. The armour may be superficial or deep-lying, soft as a sponge or hard as nails. However, in each case its function was to protect against displeasure.

41

Reichian schools of psychology have developed various forms of exercises which resemble asanas and mudras, designed to release pent-up emotions, anxieties and repressions. These exercises concentrate on releasing prana, which they call bioenergy. Thus it is similar in many respects to moola bandha and other yogic techniques. However, no abreactive, Reichian, or relaxation therapy in psychology has yet utilized the perineum in contraction, let alone the perineal body and cervix.

The technique of moola bandha had been a closely guarded secret for millennia. By contracting the mooladhara chakra we have a more powerful technique than all the modern psychological techniques put together. They look like child's play compared with a technique offering infinite bliss, knowledge and enlightenment.

We have seen many cases of severe depression clear up quickly and without emotional or psychic trauma through the practice of moola bandha even though the individuals concerned were close to suicide. They experienced old memories, emotions, and experiences, but because of training in detached awareness, the memories passed into consciousness and out again, like bubbles floating harmlessly to the surface and bursting.

So moola bandha has the potential to release us from the depressions, neuroses and other psychological problems that dampen our joy in life and prevent us from fulfilling our potential, through raising of kundalini shakti. Moola bandha is safe (when practised according to the instructions), efficient and simple. Coupled with its purgative qualities, capable of 'spring cleaning' the mental and emotional body, moola bandha is a technique to open the door to freedom, joy and liberation.

Mooladhara Chakra

Moola bandha is a psychic practice which manipulates the pranic body, especially apana, by contracting mooladhara chakra. It sends energy up to ajna and sahasrara chakras directly and thereby stimulates all the other chakras as it travels through the sushumna.

The chakras

The chakras are whirling vortices of energy which exist in the pranic (etheric) body of man at the linking points between the body and the mind. They occur at the intersection of ida and pingala in sushumna, being psychosomatic points, where mind and body touch.

There are fourteen major chakras. The seven lower chakras are: *atala, vitala, sutala, talatala, rasatala, mahatala, patala*. They represent evolution from basic atomic structures to mineral life, then plant, lower animals, and so on. The seven main chakras (*shat chakras*) are *mooladhara* (perineal body/cervix), *swadhisthana* (tip of coccyx), *manipura* (navel), *anahata* (heart), *vishuddhi* (throat), *ajna* (eyebrow centre, and closely related to mooladhara chakras), *sahasrara* (crown of the head; not always included in the shat chakras because it does not lie within the *merudanda* – spinal cord). Each higher chakra represents a more subtle frequency of pranic energy and a higher level of consciousness. They are like switches which turn on different parts of our psychophysiological mechanism.

In 1927, the Reverend Charles Leadbetter, a noted Theosophist, wrote a book called *The Chakras*, based largely on his own psychic perceptions, in which he described the chakras as follows:

"When quite undeveloped they appear as small circles about two inches in diameter, glowing fully in the ordinary man; but when awakened and vivified they are seen as blazing, coruscating whirlpools, much increased in size, and resembling miniature suns. If we imagine ourselves to be looking straight down into the bell of a flower of the convolvulus type we shall get some idea of the general appearance of a chakra. The stalk of the flower in each springs from a point in the spine.

All these wheels are perpetually rotating, and into the hub or open mouth of each, force from the higher world is always flowing. Without this inrush of energy the physical body could not exist."

The concept of chakra is common to many traditions. There also exists an interesting and exact correlation between the chakras and the kyo shos or pressure points in one branch of esoteric Japanese *judo*. They also correspond exactly to acupuncture points seated in the spine and acupressure points massaged in *shiatzu*, (a form of therapy from Japan). The chakras have been symbolized by many of the great religions and spiritual societies of the world: Judaism, Christianity, Islam, Egyptian, Kabbalists, Rosicrucians, and so on.

The meaning of each chakra can never be fully explained in words, especially the higher chakras. They must be experienced to be understood, but at the same time, there are general attributes associated with each chakra. There is a great deal of symbology to be found in the ancient yogic texts which should not be misunderstood to represent the actual experience of the chakras. They symbolize and express the experiences one feels when the chakras are stimulated and awakened.

Mooladhara chakra

Mooladhara chakra marks the interface between two modes of evolution as it is the lowest chakra in man but the highest in animals. Man, therefore, stands one octave higher than the animal. By stimulating this chakra via the practice of moola bandha we can raise ourselves higher again as the kundalini rises through the psychic centres or chakras, lifting our consciousness to the level of the divine.

The following are a few of the basic attributes associated with mooladhara chakra, which is stimulated and awakened through the practice of moola bandha. Mooladhara is the centre where one is concerned with obtaining personal security, the main motive of life being to obtain food, a place to live and so on. In this centre the individual fights the world and sees it as totally alien to him. According to Samkhya philosophy, mooladhara is symbolic of the earth element, and is closely related to the sense of smell and motion of the legs. Each chakra is said to have eighteen attributes.

Characteristics of mooladhara

1. There are four petals which correspond to the number of nadis in this particular centre.
2. The colour of the petals is red.
3. The letters of the Sanskrit alphabet representing the four petals or the *nadis* are *wam, sham, sham, sam*, (वं,शं,षं,सं)
4. The *tattwa*, or element, of mooladhara is *prithvi*, earth.
5. The yantra or shape, which is the visual representation of the tattwa, is a square.
6. The colour of the yantra is yellow.
7. The *beeja mantra*, the seed sound or vibration of the tattwa, is *lam*.
8. A seven-trunked elephant depicts the characteristics of the tattwa. The devi is pictured astride the animal, or the aspirant may picture himself upon its back. It is a vehicle of the consciousness at this particular plane.
9. The *devi*, representing the dhatus or bodily substances, is *Dakini* or *Savitri*, the creator, red-eyed and fearsome.

45

10. The *deva*, male aspect of mooladhara, is *Ganesha*.
11. The *loka*, or world within, corresponding to the world without, is *bhu*, the world of death.
12. The *granthi*, or psychic knot, which when broken releases intoxicating nectar, is *brahma granthi*. Associated with it is a linga symbolizing the male principle interlocked with the female and creative cause.
13. The *indriya*, or sense, is smell.
14. The *jnanendriya*, or organ of sense, is the nose.
15. The *karmendriya*, or organ of action, is the anus.
16. The location in the *sthula sharira* or gross body is two fingers above the anus, between the reproductive and excretory systems.
17. The physical correspondence of the chakra is the sacro-coccygeal plexus.
18. The powers gained through the awakening of the centre are full knowledge of kundalini and the power to awaken it, levitation, control over the breath, mind, semen, ability to produce any scent, fragrant or foul, for oneself and others.

Mooladhara chakra is the base chakra in man. It has, however, a direct link with ajna chakra situated in the mid-brain. Thus, by stimulating this centre through moola bandha we also awaken our intuitive faculties associated with the third eye, the eye of intuition.

When we remember that mooladhara chakra represents the instinctive, animalistic side of man and that when man's consciousness resides here he is unconscious of himself, then we can understand how an awakening in this chakra means an awakening of the individual to his instincts and animal propensities.

Animal consciousness is basically unconscious, as they are not aware, and do not know that they exist. Man, however, is able to know that he exists, and to experience the world at a conscious level, at least for brief periods of time. Those who are aware for longer periods are more evolved in terms of consciousness, and those who are constantly aware twenty-four hours a day have completed their human evolution and can exist as conscious entities without the need for physical bodies. This stage is called *jivanmukta* and occurs when kundalini pierces sahasrara chakra.

By the practice of moola bandha, the unconscious, instinctive, uncontrolled, selfish, violent, animal propensities are transformed into intuition, control, selflessness, peace and divine qualities. This transformation takes place with the union of consciousness and prana, just as carbon becomes a diamond, shining with its own inner light. This is the potential that awaits us in mooladhara chakra in the form of kundalini shakti, when awakened under the expert guidance of a spiritual master.

When moola bandha is perfected, kundalini awakens. The apana which normally moves downward is reversed and is united with prana. Nada, the cosmic sound *Aum*, joins with bindu. Form and formless unify. The aspirant travels on the path of involution (*nivritti*) riding the serpent power until he pierces the bindu and enters into sahasrara chakra, thus achieving perfection in yoga. This is obviously the final stage for the yogi, culmination in expansion of consciousness to the cosmic sphere and liberation. He is freed from the bonds of life and death, gaining immortality. The wheel of karma ceases, which means that all movement ceases. When apana and prana merge the pranas of the body stop functioning, the fluctuations of mind cease, ego dissolves and ignorance is replaced by knowledge. The world stops, creation dissolves and we experience pure consciousness, dynamic equilibrium, samadhi.

Kundalini Awakening

Kundalini arousal can take place with awakening of any one of the chakras, though traditionally it occurs with the opening of mooladhara chakra which is stimulated by moola bandha. Thus it is said that moola bandha is the trigger which activates the arousal of kundalini. The word kundalini is derived from two Sanskrit words, kundala and kunda. *Kundala* means 'coiled' and *kunda* means 'a pit'. Thus kundalini is symbolized as a snake, *bhujangi*, residing in a deeper place, mooladhara chakra. It is coiled around a *shivalingam*, the symbol of creation, and represents the potential energy residing in man. In English, kundalini may be translated as the 'primal power' or as Sir John Woodroffe calls it 'the serpent power'.

The concept of kundalini is well-known through various world cultures. Some African tribesmen known as the Kung people refer to it as 'n/um'. To the Chinese it was known as 'spiritual fire', and to the American Indians as 'hurakan'. More recently it has been referred to as 'universal electric energy'. No matter what it is called the underlying principle is essentially the same.

In *The Serpent Power* by Sir John Woodroffe it is stated that: "Kundalini is *sabda brahman* or 'the word' (*vak, nada*) in bodies and is in her own form (*svaroopa*) pure consciousness and is all powers (*sarva-saktimayi*)... She is in fact the cosmic energy in bodies and as such the cause of all, and though

48

manifesting as, is not confined to any of her products. She is called the serpent and she sleeps in mooladhara. She sleeps because she is at rest. Then man's consciousness is awake to the world, her creation in which she is immanent. When she is awake and yoga is complete, man sleeps to the world and enjoys superworldly experience."

The mind is illuminated in stages as the kundalini rises through the spinal cord, piercing the chakras. It does not actually travel through each chakra one by one, but ascends the sushumna to the brain and sahasrara chakra where all the chakras are situated. It actually works on them at a psychophysiological level, that is, on the brain and mind simultaneously.

The scriptures indicate that in order for kundalini to achieve its final upward movement to sahasrara it must first pierce through three major *granthis* (psychic knots) These are *brahma granthi, vishnu granthi* and *rudra granthi*, situated in mooladhara, anahata and ajna chakras respectively. Each granthi represents a particular state of consciousness, or attachment, which acts as an obstacle on the path to higher awareness.

1. **Brahma granthi**, situated in mooladhara chakra, symbolizes attachment to possessions – body, material objects, etc. It is associated with feelings of lethargy and ignorance, and manifests as severe limitations in the ability to act.
2. **Vishnu granthi**, situated in anahata chakra, symbolizes attachment to people including relatives and friends.
3. **Rudra granthi**, situated in ajna chakra, symbolizes attachment to psychic visions and powers (*siddhis*).

Kundalini cannot begin or continue to rise until the granthis are pierced or, in other words, attachment is broken.

The scriptures go on to state that by the practice of the three bandhas (moola, uddiyana and jalandhara) the sixteen adharas are closed. *Adhara* means 'a support, a vital part.' The sixteen vital parts are the big toes, ankles, knees, thighs, prepuce, organs of generation, navel, heart, neck, throat, palate, nose, the middle of the eyebrows, forehead, head

49

and *brahmarandhra* (the aperture in the crown of the head through which the soul is said to leave the body at death). When the sixteen adharas are closed, the consciousness becomes completely introverted with no means of escape, and meditation spontaneously takes place. Thus moola bandha helps us to gain deeper internal meditative states. It also pierces brahma granthi, liberating us from attachment and taking us inward.

Conversely, moola bandha can occur spontaneously in meditation. If this happens, feel no concern, do not attempt to consciously control the activity in the pelvic floor. Simply be aware of the sensation (both physical and mental) and continue with your meditation.

Spontaneous moola bandha is more likely to occur when the breath becomes very slow and shallow. As the mind grows tranquil so too inhalation and exhalation tend to equalize until at the point of perfect balance the breath stops; kumbhaka and moola bandha occur and expansion of consciousness takes place.

Through the practice of moola bandha the yogi attempts to reach the source or 'moola' of all creation. His goal is the complete restraint (*bandha*) of the patterns of consciousness (*chitta*) which include the mind (*manas*), intellect (*buddhi*) and the ego (*ahamkara*). Through controlled restraint, he achieves union with the universal flow.

In the words of Wilhelm Reich: "Once we open up to the flow of the energy within our own body, we also open up to the flow of energy in the universe."

The spine is often symbolized in yogic literature as a lotus with its roots at the base and flowering in the brain. Kabbalistic and theosophical literature is also based upon the concept of the 'tree of life', which was normally depicted in a similar fashion. Sometimes the kriya yoga practice of *tadan kriya* (beating mooladhara chakra against the ground while performing moola bandha) is interpreted as stimulating the roots of the tree of life, thereby injecting the body and mind with the vitality of kundalini.

As long as kundalini remains in the chakras, it gives energy to various organs of the physical body. But once it ascends to the level of the brahmarandhra quite another process and a very interesting one begins. This is when one gains vivid insights into the various constituents (said to be 17 in number) of the subtle body and the deeper knowledge of these entities unfolds. Thus, after kundalini awakens and illumines the various chakras, another process of illumination starts. Although we are preparing for the awakening of the chakras and the kundalini, this is only the first stage. It is not the end, it is only the beginning. One must go on higher and higher into the realms of spiritual illumination.

Two classical yogic accounts of the experience of kundalini are offered here by Swami Narayananda and Paramahamsa Ramakrishna.

In *The Primal Power* Swami Narayananda describes the experience: "There is a burning up the back and over the whole body. Kundalini's entrance into sushumna (the central spinal canal) occurs with pain in the back... One feels a creeping sensation from the toes and sometimes it shakes the whole body. The rising is felt like that of an ant creeping up slowly over the body towards the head. Its ascent is felt like the wriggling of a snake or a bird hopping from place to place."

In *A Mythic Image* by Joseph Campbell, the experience of Ramakrishna is given in strikingly similar terms: "There are five kinds of samadhi (spiritual rapture). In these samadhis one feels the sensation of the spiritual current (kundalini) to be like the movement of an ant, a fish, a monkey, a bird or a serpent. Sometimes the spiritual current rises through the spine, crawling like an ant. Sometimes, in samadhi, the soul swims joyfully in the ocean of divine ecstasy like a fish. Sometimes, when I lie down on my side, I feel the spiritual current pushing me like a monkey and playing with me joyfully. I remain still. That current, like a monkey, suddenly with one jump reaches the sahasrara. That is why you see me jump with a start. Sometimes again, the spiritual current

51

rises like a bird hopping from one branch to another. The place where it rests feels like fire... Sometimes the spiritual current moves up like a snake. Going in a zigzag way, at last it reaches the head and I go into samadhi. A man's spiritual consciousness is not awakened unless his kundalini is aroused."

In the kundalini yoga tradition, Swami Muktananda has published an autobiography in which he gives graphic descriptions of sensations, involuntary movements, flows of energy through the body, unusual breathing patterns, inner lights and sounds, formed visions and voices and many other extraordinary experiences, leading on to intense rapture and bliss.

Swami Yogeshwarananda, a well-known and respected Himalayan yogi, in his "Address to the 5th Convention of the International Association of Religion and Parapsychology", (Japan), gives the following account of his experience of kundalini arousal: "...and then came the great moment of my life. My guru performed trataka, that is he fixed his gaze on my forehead, and I went into a trance. I forgot about my body, about the surroundings. I forgot even the presence of the great yogi before me. I do not know how long I continued... it was a state of timelessness, but at one stage in this experience there was at the base of the sacral plexus, mooladhara chakra, the emergence of a great light which showed me in clear detail the whole anatomy and physiology of my body, as if someone had opened up my skin and with the help of a torch was showing me every nook and corner of my physical body. After this experience, the gross physical body retreated into the background of consciousness and the next stage started, the experience of the chakras... At the second stage there emerged at the base of the plexus another sort of light. The first, which showed me every detail of the anatomy, was yellowish. Now this was a bluish-white colour... During that seven hour trance I experienced various things: one was a light which illumined a triangular shape... another was a light in a spinal cord, it entered the

52

sushumna nadi and moved upwards illumining every chakra which appeared to have petals like flowers."

Descriptions of the kundalini experience are becoming increasingly more common in modern scientific literature. Likewise the phenomena of kundalini awakening is becoming much more apparent in technologically developing countries. However, due to the personal intimacy of the experience, it is difficult to objectify. Lee Sannella in *Kundalini – Psychosis or Transcendence* gives the following collection of sensations and happenings culled from the many personal experiences he has documented.

- **Spontaneous movements**: unaccustomed body postures, or even classical hatha yogasanas. Any part of the body can be affected by smooth, sinuous, spasmodic, jerky or vibratory movements. Occasionally the body may lock into one position, but this is usually temporary and ceases when the meditation is over.
- **Breathing pattern**: spontaneous pranayama, breath retention, shallow breathing, deep breathing, rapid breathing, may all occur.
- **Body sensations**: throbbing in mooladhara chakra area; the spontaneous contraction of moola bandha; tingling; vibration; itch or tickle; orgasmic, all-embracing sensations; heat and cold of differing degrees; pain in the spine, eyes, head and other body parts occurs especially when the body is not adequately purified.
- **Internal sounds**: whistling, hissing, chirping, flute-like sounds, ocean, surf, thunder, brook murmurs, the crackle of fire, drums, conch shell sounds, bells and roaring have been reported.
- **Changes in the thought process**: thoughts may speed up, slow down or stop altogether. They may seem out of balance, strange or irrational. Some people report that they feel close to insanity in this experience or may enter trance states devoid of all thought. These experiences are only temporary however, representing cleansing of mind and body.

- **Detachment**: the individual may feel that he or she is watching what is happening, including his or her own ideas, thoughts and feelings from a distance, like one detached. It differs from aloofness or anxious withdrawal in that it is a dissociation of the separate observer self from the mental activities that it observes. One's activities may continue as usual, and thus this condition may not interfere with normal functioning.
- **Dissociation**: when the withdrawal of the self from active involvement or identification with what it perceives is attained, a state of detachment occurs. But when it is not in balance, due to deep psychological resistances, to fear and confusions, or to social and other environmental pressures, then negative aspects of the experience may be emphasized. However, given time and the proper environmental support, the imbalance is overcome and one finds a more suitable focus for his or her energies as the negative symptoms vanish.
- **Unusual or extreme emotions**: feelings of ecstasy, bliss, peace, love, devotion, joy and cosmic harmony may occur, but also intense fear, anxiety, depression, hatred and confusion. Especially in the early stages of the process, any of the normal emotions may be experienced with much greater intensity than usual. Later on feelings of peace, love and contentment tend to predominate.
- **Psychic experiences**: out of the body experiences, seeing oneself as larger than the normal size of one's body, ESP (that is obtaining information through means other than the known physical senses), divine smells, divine touch, divine visions (of one's guru or of gods).
- **Single seeing**: this interesting variation in the visual function can be easily identified as a separate and distinct state by the typical and graphic metaphors used to describe the experience.

In *An Experience of Enlightenment* Flora Courtois writes: "My sight had changed, sharpened to an infinitely small point which moved ceaselessly in paths totally free of the old accustomed ones, as if flowing from a new source. It was as if some inner eye... which extended without limit... had been restored... focused on infinity in a way that was detached from immediate sight and yet had a profound effect on sight... there was a sharp one-pointedness to my attention now rooted into some deeper centre so that by everyday sight, my eyes, were released from their need to see the world outside... no matter where I looked no shadow (image) of my nose ever appeared in the clear field of sight."

This experience is also described in the *New Testament* (Luke 11:34): "The light of the body is the eye; therefore when thine eye is single thy whole body is also full of light."

To the uninitiated and those lacking experience in such matters, the above symptoms may sound like those of a psychotic experience. Many people undergoing an 'awakening' have been suspected of going 'insane'. Now, however, the medical profession is slowly becoming aware of the differences between derangement and expansion of mental faculties and many doctors are setting up clinics to help people through such times of crisis. It is easy to understand that a person experiencing spontaneous breath retention (*kevala kumbhaka*), the eyes fixing on the eyebrow centre (*shambhavi mudra*), or a sensation of absence of the physical body, may experience fear which would then distort and disturb the process.

There are a few facts to be remembered when we consider the above manifestations of kundalini shakti.

• They are very rare.
• When the aspirant is under the guidance of a guru or master such manifestations are easily held in perspective and handled.
• Utilizing the proper sequence of practices, training under a master, and going slowly along the spiritual path makes the process of bodily purification easy and simple. The attendant manifestations are thereby reduced and may not occur at all before the stage of enlightening peace and wisdom.

- After the manifestations have passed, the subject is left in the state of bliss, peace and higher consciousness.

The aftermath of this experience is such that all doubts disappear and your body becomes as light as air. You possess an inexhaustible energy for work, a balanced mind amidst all the trials and tribulations of life, and you understand the hidden secrets of life. All this is attainable through the use of moola bandha if it is used correctly, with discrimination and combined with other practices.

For kundalini to rise, the body must be able to cope with its force and the nervous system must be strong, healthy and mature. This is attained through yogic practice. When preparations are complete, kundalini will rise spontaneously of its own accord, liberating and expanding the consciousness. When you awaken your kundalini you stand on the threshold of infinity.

Carl G. Jung, eminent Swiss psychiatrist, sums up this experience in his *Psychological Commentary on Kundalini Yoga* where he states: "When you succeed in awakening the kundalini so that it starts to move out of its mere potentiality, you necessarily experience a world which is totally different from our world. It is a world of eternity."

Kundalini represents the underlying unity of all creation. It is the medium of existence and the final fulfilment of truth. Concerning its awakening there are two important points that every aspirant should keep in mind. Firstly, it is possible to manifest similar symptoms to those mentioned above during the practice of moola bandha. The same may also be hallucinated under the influence of drugs, therefore one should carefully and honestly examine experiences that may arise.

Secondly, the arousal of kundalini involves psychic phenomena, but is primarily a spiritual experience. Many people assume that kundalini awakening leads to psychic abilities, powers and supernormal phenomena. Though this may be true in some cases, it is dangerous to overemphasize psychic powers and to play with them. Psychic ability is not

56

a prerequisite for kundalini awakening and the growth and evolution of consciousness.

One must always keep in mind that this energy is the key to spiritual rebirth and brings about a dramatic change in one's life. It is a force to be respected and revered, and was for millennia treasured as the secret elixir of immortal life unavailable to the masses. Today, through practices such as moola bandha, its awakening is within the reach of everyone. Kundalini is the hidden key to the realization of one's own essential nature and may be actualized through the perfection of moola bandha.

In *Kundalini: The Evolutionary Energy in Man*, Gopi Krishna says: "This mechanism, known as kundalini, is the real cause of all genuine spiritual phenomena, the biological basis of evolution and development of personality, the secret origin of all esoteric and occult doctrines, the master key to the unsolved mystery of creation, the inexhaustible source of philosophy, art and science and the fountainhead of all religions, past, present, and future."

Practices

Moola Bandha in Perspective

It is necessary for the yoga student to view moola bandha in perspective. The sequence of yoga practices traditionally taught with moola bandha is as follows:
1. Yamas – rules of social conduct, observances
2. Niyamas – personal disciplines, restraints
3. Shatkarmas – cleansing techniques
4. Asanas – physical postures
5. Pranayama – breathing exercises
6. Uddiyana bandha – abdominal contraction
7. Ashwini mudra – anal contraction
8. Moola bandha – perineal/cervical contraction
9. Vajroli mudra – urethral contraction.

To become worthy of the guru's teachings the student traditionally had to fulfil certain moral requirements, called yamas and niyamas, which were also prerequisite to the study of yoga. In Patanjali's *Yoga Sutras* they are listed as follows:

Yamas: non-violence, truth, honesty, sensual abstinence and non-possessiveness are the five self-restraints.

Niyamas: cleanliness, contentment, austerity, self-study and resignation to God constitute the fixed observances.

The yamas were designed to harmonize one's social interactions, while niyamas were intended to harmonize one's feelings. Together, the yamas and niyamas were taught in order to reduce friction between one's outer actions and inner attitudes.

61

When a student had adequately fulfilled these requirements (which usually took a few years) he was then introduced to the shatkarmas. In the *Gherand Samhita* it is written: "Dhauti, basti, neti, lauliki (nauli), trataka and kapalbhati are the six kriyas popularly known as shatkarmas." (GS, 1:12)

The shatkarmas are purification techniques. Before any long journey is undertaken adequate preparations must be made to ensure its success. However, even with all the other preparations completed, if the person undertaking the journey has not adequately prepared himself physically and mentally, the journey must be cancelled or, if continued, may end in failure. Similarly, on the spiritual path adequate physical and mental preparations must be made. This is done by the practice of the shatkarmas whereby the body is purified and revitalized, ensuring an endurance and steadfastness necessary to complete one's lifelong spiritual journey.

After the body is cleansed it must be strengthened and balanced. This is done at the next stage of the sadhaka's development by the practice of yogasanas, as stated in the *Gherand Samhita*: "Asanas are as many as there are numbers of varieties of creatures in the world. According to Lord Shiva the total number of yogasanas is eighty-four lakh (8,400,000). Out of eighty-four lakh, however, only eighty-four yogasanas are important for the good and welfare of man." (GS, 2:1–2)

Once the student was reasonably proficient at maintaining the asana for lengthy periods of time, he was next introduced to the practices of pranayama (breathing exercises), this being perhaps his first insight into the more subtle aspects of yoga. Where the shatkarmas and asanas purify the body physically, the practices of pranayama purify the body on a pranic level, as stated in the *Hatha Yoga Pradipika*: "By removing the impurities of the nadis (pranic channels), the air can be retained according to one's wish, the appetite is increased, the divine sound is awakened and the body becomes healthy." (HYP, 2:1)

62

Perhaps the most important effect of nadi purification is that the yogi is now able to effectively conserve prana. The conservation of prana is vital to spiritual sadhana and was further enhanced by the practice that traditionally followed.

The student was next introduced to the concept of bandha, and consequently was taught uddiyana bandha, the foundation for more advanced work.

"Uddiyana (meaning flying up, soaring) is so-called because the great bird prana (breath), which is tied to it, flies without being fatigued. This is explained below. The belly above the navel is pressed backwards towards the spine. This uddiyana bandha is like a lion over the elephant of death. Uddiyana is always very easy when learned from a guru. The practitioner of this, if old, becomes young again. The portions above and below the navel should be drawn backward towards the spine. By practising this for six months one can undoubtedly conquer death. Uddiyana is one of the best bandhas, for by contracting it firmly, liberation comes spontaneously." (HYP, 3:54–9)

Uddiyana bandha was always taught before moola bandha, for it is said by fully contracting the abdominal muscles (with the breath exhaled) the contraction of the perineum (moola bandha) may spontaneously occur, or if not, it is very much easier.

Ashwini mudra was taught after uddiyana bandha not to break the possible continuity, but more as a preliminary practice to the powerful effects of moola bandha.

For, by the practice of moola bandha, the student was then surveying the awesome force of kundalini. For this he needed to be introduced gently into the area of the lower pelvis and ashwini mudra would take him slowly to the threshold of his new spiritual rebirth.

Moola Bandha Sadhana

The technique of moola bandha is simplicity itself and you will find this practical section is also very concise, straightforward and easy to follow. Although moola bandha may be incorporated with many other yogic techniques, we have excluded all extraneous practices in order to emphasize those directly related to the mastery of this bandha as a separate and a powerful practice in its own right. The complexities of moola bandha lie only in the location of mooladhara chakra itself, and for that reason we have included a number of preliminary practices to help you focus your awareness on the primary chakra. Certain advanced techniques for the awakening of mooladhara also serve to enhance awareness and control in moola bandha, adding an extra dimension of potency to the basic practice. These too have been included to enable the student to pursue this sadhana to the utmost.

Expert guidance
Moola bandha should ideally be learned under the expert supervision of an experienced yoga teacher. Where this is not possible you must certainly endeavour to contact a competent guide should you experience any confusion or difficulty during your solo practice. Correct guidance will prevent many of the difficulties the student could possible encounter without supervision.

If you are suffering from a heart ailment, high blood pressure, vertigo, high intracranial pressure or amenorrhoea, then you should adopt this technique, like any other, only after clearance from your doctor and a qualified yoga therapist. Generally speaking, any person with one of these problems is advised *not* to practise moola bandha until he has recovered good health. Your yoga teacher will suggest suitable substitute practices.

Physical or psychic practice
Much discussion surrounds the question of whether moola bandha is a physical or mental practice. In fact it is both, though its ultimate effect, the arousal of kundalini, can only occur on a psychic pranic level. The simple physical contraction of mooladhara's physical trigger point will not have so profound an effect as activating an infinite source of prana (kundalini). This will only manifest at far more subtle levels of consciousness beyond the range of physical awareness. However, one should not feel that physical contraction of the perineal body/cervix does not play an indispensable role in learning to master the practice of moola bandha.

The perfection of moola bandha requires the development of an acute refinement of mental and psychic awareness that allows for the localization, isolation and contraction of mooladhara chakra. This is developed in the beginning through the physical contraction of the perineal body or cervix as the case may be. We begin at the most accessible level, the tangible physical body. By combining physical contraction with mental awareness and visualization, we can then heighten our sensitivity on the psychic plane. Through the physical isolation and contraction of perineal body/cervix the mind becomes one-pointed in that area, and this allows for the finer processes of pranic stimulation. The contraction further draws the mind towards concentrating on the psychic centre in the pranic body, mooladhara chakra itself. So until the practice is mastered completely, we must take assistance of actual physical contraction.

65

Nevertheless, there does come a stage for the advanced yogi in which moola bandha is only the psychic contraction of the mooladhara chakra. The physical contraction, having achieved its purpose, is no longer necessary. When the physical and the mental aspects of the practice have been fully integrated to spark sufficient psychic sensitivity, then you will find yourself spontaneously able to contract mooladhara without any physical contraction at all. You simply direct your awareness to mooladhara, and contract the chakra by thought alone. Thus moola bandha is perfected in three stages:

1. Physical contraction only – preliminary,
2. Physical and mental contraction – intermediate,
3. Psychic contraction only – advanced.

To develop the capacity for psychic contraction of moola bandha usually takes years of regular practise but once it has been achieved, you will very quickly become established in this practice. Just the same, it is subject to fluctuation. If the mind is relaxed and one-pointed, then psychic contraction is easily effected, but if your thoughts are turbulent then you will find it more difficult. In this case use moola bandha with physical contraction to quieten the mind, then move on to the psychic bandha.

Integration with other practices

In order to master moola bandha, it must be practised as a separate sadhana in its own right, preferably by following the sequence of practices given here. Its ideal place in your yogic routine is after asanas and pranayama, but before meditation. Once perfected, moola bandha can then be performed in conjunction with many other yogic techniques. For your convenience, we have listed most of them below.

Nevertheless, it is neither necessary nor advisable to practise moola bandha on every possible occasion. This bandha is integrated with asanas and advanced pranayama only to achieve certain specific effects, and its indiscriminate use with any and every practice is a waste of time. For the correct

66

application of moola bandha in this respect, we suggest you follow the advice of your teacher or consult *Asana Pranayama Mudra Bandha*, published by Bihar School of Yoga.

Duration
The student should not fall prey to the temptation of overpractise. As in every other aspect of yogic life, the key is moderation and appropriate application. The duration of each practice is specified at the end of its description. These are the recommended number of rounds for the average working student. They are not fixed, but in general fifteen to thirty minutes daily practice is ample. You may do fewer rounds if you wish. Indeed, it is preferable to practise a few rounds every day rather than many rounds every few days. If you wish to increase the length of your practice, once again you should discuss the matter with your teacher.

Spontaneous moola bandha
Mooladhara chakra stimulation may lead to spontaneous moola bandha anywhere, anytime. When this occurs you will feel increased energy, mental clarity, and so on. This is a natural outcome of regular yogic practice culminating in expanded awareness. When it does occur it is accompanied by a blissful sensation within the whole organism, so you will know when it happens. There are certain practices which predispose to this experience, the foremost of these being meditation performed in siddhasana, siddha yoni asana, and padmasana. Of course, it can occur in any asana, pranayama, mudra or bandha. After regular practise perhaps you will be lucky enough to enjoy this experience.

Sitting position
There is no one single asana traditionally prescribed for the practice of moola bandha. Although many people associate this bandha with *moolabandhasana*, most people cannot even perform this advanced asana, let alone remain in it comfortably. Moolabandhasana is not a necessary pre-

67

requisite for moola bandha and is beyond consideration for most of us.

What is required is a steady position that may be comfortably held for some time. The back must be straight and it is desirable that a certain external pressure be applied to the perineum to enhance awareness of the mooladhara trigger point. The asanas that best fulfil these conditions are bhadrasana and siddhasana (siddha yoni asana for women). When moola bandha is practised as part of kundalini yoga kriyas, utthanpadasana is also commonly used. The details for all these asanas are given under the practices in 'Locating Mooladhara Chakra'. If these asanas cannot be used you may sit in any other comfortable posture where the knees rest firmly on the ground: padmasana, swastikasana, ardha padmasana, sukhasana, vajrasana. Sukhasana especially may be modified so that one heel presses the perineum and thus it becomes a more suitable posture for moola bandha, and one which most people can use.

Each of these asanas has specific effects, but siddha yoni asana and siddhasana are the most highly recommended positions. They provide a steady base that keeps the spine straight and relaxed while 'locking' the legs so that if one swoons or falls asleep during the practice, there is no danger of falling over. As the trunk begins to lean forward, it comes to a point where the practitioner jerks awake. Not only this, but siddhasana/siddha yoni asana check the nervous and pranic flow in the lower body, enhancing the performance of moola bandha by assisting the upward flow of these energies. These advantages, in combination with the pressure applied to the perineum, make siddhasana and siddha yoni asana ideal for the performance of moola bandha.

Nevertheless, you may find it difficult to adopt either of these postures in the beginning. Practise the pre-meditative postures in *Asana Pranayama Mudra Bandha* and gradually you will be successful. In the meantime, begin your moola bandha sadhana using bhadrasana, utthanpadasana, or any other asana where the awareness of mooladhara is enhanced.

How to know?

Perhaps the two most common questions asked by yoga students attempting to master moola bandha are:
- How can I know when I have contracted the perineal body/cervix?
- How can I know when I have perfected moola bandha?

At the start it is often difficult for the beginner to know when the perineal body/cervix is contracted. As the perineal body and cervix are both obscured from view, it is not even possible to be certain through visual inspection. However, one reliable method by which one may be sure is through the sense of touch. Obviously the method varies for male and female, therefore precise details are outlined below.

Male

In the sitting or lying position place the finger against the point approximately midway between the anus and the scrotum. Inhale and with the awareness concentrated slowly attempt to contract the perineal body. If you can feel that the point at which your finger rests has lifted upwards into the body then you have succeeded in contracting the perineal body. If this takes place without movement of the anus or penis, then be assured that you have also successfully isolated the perineal body.

Female

In the sitting or lying position, insert the finger into the vagina as far as you can. Inhale and with the awareness concentrated slowly attempt to contract the muscles around your finger. If you can distinctly feel the muscles of the upper vagina contract, then you have succeeded in contracting the area around the cervix. If you achieve this contraction without movement of the anus or the urinary opening, then you have also successfully isolated the mooladhara trigger point.

It should be understood quite clearly at this point that there is a fundamental difference between the correct performance of moola bandha and its complete mastery. Even though the cervix and perineal body can be both isolated and constricted on a physical level, this is not an indication that moola bandha has been mastered, for moola bandha is also psychic contraction; ability to mentally contract the psychic centre known as mooladhara chakra will take considerably more time to mature. The experience of complete mastery of moola bandha is distinct and definite and common to both sexes – an overwhelming sensation of 'mental orgasm' in the eyebrow centre or directly behind it in ajna chakra. This experience is one of indescribable bliss and may last for anything up to fifteen minutes.

A sadhana

Moola bandha is not just another yogic technique. It has such significance in arousal of kundalini that, in every sense, it constitutes an important tantric sadhana.

Any sadhana is like a delicate plant that, when watered regularly and patiently protected, bursts forth in brilliant fragrant flowers. So too, regular and patient practice will open the flower of the mooladhara lotus to the eternal sunshine of spiritual awakening. May every grace be showered upon you.

Locating Mooladhara Chakra

Usually when we are searching for something we are guided primarily by our eyes: we go 'looking for' that thing. Since the physical trigger point of mooladhara chakra is hidden from sight, the next easiest and most effective way to find this root centre is through touch. By adopting certain bodily poses, we can 'touch' or apply pressure to the trigger point in the physical body. This then acts as a reference point which guides our awareness to the location of the psychic centre in the subtle body.

There are several asanas which will cause a stretch or contraction in the pelvic floor that enables us to feel a distinct touch at the mooladhara trigger point. We can then direct our awareness to that point, and from there to the chakra itself. However, in order to 'pull the trigger' of mooladhara, the asana must be performed fully and correctly. We should be capable of relaxing into the pose so that our attention is free to go in search of mooladhara. Of course, you will be able to master some asanas more easily than others, so we suggest you try them all to determine which are the most comfortable. Furthermore, each of the given positions exerts a slightly different pressure and so you should try them all to find the one that is most effective for your personality.

Asanas recommended for location of mooladhara chakra are uttanpadasana, bhadrasana, siddhasana or siddha yoni asana, pada prasar paschimottanasana, hanumanasana, moolabandhasana, gorakshasana and also koormasana.

We can also 'touch' mooladhara with sound vibration, such as those generated in bhramari pranayama and mooladhara anusandhana. We suggest that you perform one or both of these after your asana practice, and then move directly into mooladhara dhyana. This sequence thus forms a completely integrated sadhana program leading you through asana, pranayama and concentration to meditation.

BSY ©

Utthanpadasana (stretched leg pose)

Sit on the floor with both legs stretched in front of the body.

Fold the right leg under the body so that you are sitting on the right foot.

The right heel should press the perineum (or the entrance to the vagina).

The left leg remains outstretched.

Bend forwards just enough to hold the left big toe with both hands.

Do not bend the knee.

This asana may also be performed with the leg left leg folded into the perineum and the right leg outstretched.

Simplified version: Sit with the legs stretched out in front of the body.

Fold the right leg, placing heel against the perineum. The right sole rests against the inside of the left thigh, and the right knee projects at a right angle to the left leg. The left leg remains outstretched, knee to the floor. Bend forward just enough to hold the left big toe.

This asana may also be performed with the left heel pressing the perineum and the right leg outstretched.

Bhadrasana (gracious pose)

Sit in vajrasana and separate the knees as far as possible. Keeping the toes touching, but separate the feet enough to allow the buttocks to rest flat on the floor.

Ensure there is contact between the perineum and the floor. If there is not, then place a small cushion or a rolled blanket between the body and the floor so that pressure is felt at the mooladhara trigger point.

If necessary, separate the feet completely so that they lie directly beside the hips.

Straighten the spine, rest the hands on the knees, palms down, and gaze at the nosetip.

73

Siddhasana (accomplished pose for men)
>   Sit with the legs outstretched.
>   Fold the left leg and place the sole of its foot flat against the right thigh with the heel pressing the perineum, the area between the genitals and the anus.
>   Fold the right leg and place its foot on top of the left calf. Press the pelvic bone with the right heel directly above the genitals.
>   Push the toes and the other edge of this foot into the space between the left calf and thigh muscles. It may be necessary to move and replace the left leg for this.
>   Grasp the left toes, either from above or below the left calf and move them upward into the space between the right thigh and calf.
>   The legs should now be locked with the knees on the ground and the right heel directly above the left heel.
>   Make the spine steady, straight and erect, as though it were planted in the ground.
>
> **Practice note**: Siddhasana may be practised with either leg uppermost and is always done in conjunction with jnana or chin mudra. Many aspirants, especially beginners, find it easier to maintain siddhasana for long periods when their buttocks are slightly elevated by a cushion.

74

BSY ©

Siddha Yoni Asana (accomplished pose for women)
    Sit with the legs outstretched.

    Fold the left leg and place the sole of the foot flat against the inner right thigh.

    Place the heel inside the labia majora of the vagina.

    Fold the right leg and place its foot on the top of the left calf and thigh, and pull the left toes up into the space between the calf and thigh.

    Make the spine fully erect and straight as though it were planted solidly in the earth at the bottom.

Practice note: Siddha yoni asana can be practised with either leg uppermost, and is best done in conjunction with jnana mudra.

    Many practitioners, especially beginners, find this pose easiest to assume and to maintain for long periods of time if they place a low cushion under the buttocks.

BSY ©

Pada Prasar Paschimottanasana (legs spread back stretch pose)

Sit with the legs spread as wide apart as possible.

Breathe in, straighten the spine, rest the hands on the knees.

Breathing out, slide the hands from the knees to feet, and bend the body forward from the base of the spine.

Bring the forehead to the floor between the legs.

The arms should be fully extended with the hands holding the big toes.

Make sure the knees are not bent, and that the feet are turned slightly outwards.

Hold the final pose and breathe naturally.

This asana may alternatively be performed with the hands clasped and raised behind the back.

This variation is helpful for beginners who have difficulty bringing the forehead to the floor, but is less comfortable to retain for long periods of time.

Hanumanasana (Hanuman's pose)

Kneel on the left knee, right foot beside the left knee, palms of the hands flat on the floor on each side of the body.

Gradually, without any undue strain, slide the right foot forward and the left foot backward as far as it is comfortable. Support the weight on the hands.

Practise until you can lower the buttocks to the floor.

Place the palms together in front of the chest.

Moolabandhasana (perineal contraction pose)

Assume a sitting position with legs outstretched.

Bend the knees and bring the feet together at the perineum.

Raise the body onto the heels so that the heels press the perineum.

The heels can either point forward or backward.

Release and then repeat when all tension has left the legs and feet.

Gorakshanasana (Yogi Gorakhnath's pose)

Assume a sitting position.

Place the heels together as for moolabandhasana.

Instead of placing the heels under the perineum, raise them toward the navel keeping the toes on the floor.

Cross the wrists in front of the navel and hold the heels, the right fingers on the left heel and the left fingers on the right heel.

Straighten the spine and face forward.

Searching for mooladhara (for women)

Adopt any of the recommended asanas.

Relax your body completely and close your eyes.

Move your awareness to the lower part of the body and focus your attention on the contact point between your heel (or floor or cushion) and the opening of the vagina.

Become intensely aware of the slight but distinct pressure at this point.

Centre yourself at the pressure point.

Now become aware of your natural breath. Feel or imagine that you are breathing in and out of the pressure point.

Continue this for ten deep breaths.

Now bring your awareness inside the body.

From the point of external pressure, move your awareness in towards the base of the spine.

Follow the natural formation of the vagina, moving up at a slight angle and back towards the spine until you come to the opening of the womb.

You are at the opening of the womb, about two or three centimetres inside the body, about two or three centimetres above the floor, just below the base of the spine.

Focus your awareness at this point and begin to breathe in and out from the cervix to the point of outer pressure.

Breathe in and bring your awareness to the opening of the womb.

Breathe out and move again to the outer pressure point. Somewhere in this area you will find your point for mooladhara chakra.

If at first you cannot pinpoint the chakra, continue the practice for five minutes and then move to another asana.

If you so locate mooladhara, mark the spot in your consciousness by visualizing a bright yellow square and inside the square, a red triangle pointing downwards.

See this clearly and distinctly while you breathe in and out of this internal trigger point.

Continue for up to five minutes and then move to the next practice.

80

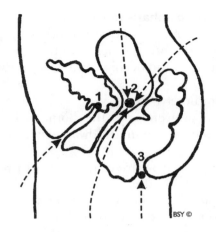

Fig. 1: Female body – location of psychic points for (1) sahajoli mudra (2) moola bandha (3) ashwini mudra

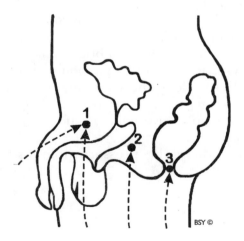

Fig. 2: Male body – location of psychic points for (1) vajroli mudra, (2) moola bandha (3) ashwini mudra

Searching for mooladhara (for men)

Sit in siddhasana or one of the other asanas where the heel is pressed into the perineum.

Close your eyes and become aware of your whole physical body.

Relax completely.

Move your awareness to the point of contact between the heel and perineum, midway between the testes and the anus.

Become intensely aware of the distinct pressure exerted on the perineal body.

Centre yourself at the pressure point.

Now become aware of your breath.

Feel or imagine that you are breathing in and out of this pressure point.

Feel the breath moving through the perineal body, becoming finer and finer, so that it pierces the point where mooladhara chakra is.

You will feel it as a psychophysical contraction.

If you locate mooladhara, mark the spot in your consciousness by visualizing a bright yellow square, and inside the square, a red triangle pointing downward.

Visualize this while at the same time breathing in and out of the trigger point in the perineal body.

Continue for up to five minutes and then move on to the next practice.

Remember where the pressure point is for future reference.

Bhramari Pranayama (humming bee breath)

Sit in bhadrasana or siddhasana/siddha yoni asana.

If these are not comfortable use any meditative asana.

Straighten the spine and hold the head erect.

Close the eyes and relax the body.

Block both ears with the index fingers.

Take a long, deep breath through the nose.

Keeping the mouth closed, separate the teeth and relax the jaw.

Then breathe out with a loud humming sound like that of a bee.

The exhalation should be slow and steady: *m-m-m-m-m-m-m-m*. The louder the better.

Feel the sound vibrating in the head.

This is one round.

In subsequent rounds, become aware of the sound piercing the midbrain, piercing through the very centre of the brain up to the crown of the head, and down towards the throat.

Extend your awareness so that the sound seems to pass straight through the centre of the body, from ajna chakra (midbrain) to mooladhara chakra.

Start with five rounds and gradually increase up to twenty.

Mooladhara Anusandhana (discovery of mooladhara)

Sit in bhadrasana, siddhasana/siddha yoni asana or any other comfortable position in which the heel presses the perineum.

Straighten the spine and hold the head erect.

Relax the body and close the eyes.

For a few moments witness your natural breath.

Then focus your awareness in the region of mooladhara chakra.

Now breathe in deeply.

On a low note, chant the mantra *lam* as you slowly exhale.

Chant continuously and rhythmically until exhalation is complete: *lam – lam – lam – lam – lam – lam.*

Run one repetition into the other in a mala of unbroken sound, and feel the vibrations resonating in mooladhara chakra.

This is one round – practise 15 rounds.

Now inhale deeply and exhale in one long, smooth chant: *lam-m-m-m-m-m-m-m-m-m.* The long 'm' sound should taper off as exhalation is completed.

Feel the resonance in mooladhara, and try to pinpoint the exact location of the chakra.

Practise 15 rounds and move straight into mooladhara dhyana.

Mooladhara Dhyana (mooladhara meditation)

Following directly on from mooladhara anusandhana, intensify your awareness of the mooladhara trigger point.

Become acutely sensitive to the chakra itself.

Now bring to your inner eye the image of an elephant.

Huge grey elephant, still and massive.

An elephant – symbol of solidarity and strength.

This elephant has seven trunks. See them clearly.

They are the seven chakras of instinctive existence where consciousness resided before reaching mooladhara chakra; becoming human.

84

Huge grey elephant with seven trunks and yourself sitting on his back.

Now flash to a yellow square... simple square, bright yellow.

Bright yellow square... yantra of the element earth.

And a sense of smell.

Merge into the bright yellow square and smell the sandalwood fragrance of your psychic body...

Bright yellow square... bright yellow body...

Within this square is a red triangle pointing downwards.

Red triangle, yantra of kundalini shakti, primal energy.

Red triangle... red triangle.

Within the triangle a smoky shivalingam, shivalingam... entwined around it is a serpent with three and a half coils.

The serpent's head is pointing upwards, towards sahasrara, the crown of spiritual experience.

Now expand your vision outward.

See mooladhara as a dark red lotus.

A lotus with four red petals.

Slowly the lotus begins to turn... four red petals going around and around... spinning lotus... whirling red vortex of primal energy.

See yourself being drawn into this spinning whirlpool of energy.

Merge into it, feel this vibrant energy pulsing through you... the sense of fullness.

After some time this vision will spontaneously fade away.

Then become aware of your breath, the natural breath.

Deepen the breath and at the same time become aware of your body... see yourself sitting in meditation... awareness of the whole body.

Chant *om* three times, then slowly open your eyes.

This is the end of mooladhara dhyana.

Note to teachers: Students may be introduced to this practice as a visualization sequence in yoga nidra.

For the Isolation of Mooladhara

For the perfection of moola bandha it is necessary that the muscles associated with the mooladhara trigger point be freely contracted. However, only these muscles must be contracted – the rest of the body remains completely relaxed. Beginners usually have difficulty both in isolating and contracting the mooladhara trigger point, but regular performance of the following techniques will overcome the difficulty.

Pelvic floor awareness

Sit in any comfortable meditation posture.
Keep the spine straight and the head upright.
Close your eyes and relax.
Your breath is natural and relaxed.
Become aware of the lower pelvic region.
Focus your attention on the pelvic floor.
Now contract this area.
The whole pelvic floor – urinary system, genitals and anus.
And relax.
Again contract.
And relax.
Do not make any attempt to separate the various muscle groups. Simply contract all the muscles in this area.
Then relax.

Check that the rest of the body is relaxed and the breath normal.
There should be no tension in any other part of the body.
Only the pelvic floor – contract and relax.
Simple, rhythmic contraction of the whole pelvic floor... tighten, release... tighten, release... tighten, release.
Continue for twenty-five rounds.
Now tighten and hold the contraction for as long as possible.
Systematically move your awareness from the anus to the genitals, making sure that each and every muscle is fully contracted.
Be aware of the contraction. How does it feel?
At what points is the pressure of contraction strongest?
Now release slowly.
Next, coordinate this contraction and relaxation with the natural breath.
As you breathe in, contract the pelvic floor.
As you breathe out, slowly relax the whole area.
Long, deep breath in and contract.
Hold the contraction for an instant at the peak of inhalation.
Breath out slowly, evenly, and gradually relax.
This is one round. Practise twenty-five rounds.

Sthul (physical) Moola Bandha
Sit in any meditative posture that applies some pressure to the mooladhara trigger point.
Close the eyes and relax the body.
Spontaneous, natural breath.
Focus your attention on the mooladhara trigger point.
Now contract mooladhara.
And relax.
Contract – relax.
Brief contraction and relaxation of mooladhara, as rhythmically and evenly as possible.

Mooladhara: contract... relax... contract... relax... contract... relax... contract... relax.
Continue for twenty five rounds.
Now slowly contract mooladhara and hold.
This contraction should be slow and gradual.
Natural breath, do not hold your breath.
Simply tighten mooladhara and hold the contraction.
Be aware only of the physical contraction. Be totally aware of the physical sensation.
Contract a little tighter... tighter... tighter.
Try to contract only the muscles associated with mooladhara.
In the beginning you will find that the anal and urinary sphincters also contract.
As you develop greater awareness and control, this will be minimized and eliminated.
Remember, intense awareness of mooladhara and contraction.
Check that the rest of the body is relaxed.
There should be no tightness in the muscles of the face, the abdomen, the inner thighs or the buttocks.
Contraction of mooladhara, the body in repose, natural breath.
Now relax slowly and evenly.
You might find that you are unable to release the contraction gradually – that it happens all of a sudden.
Greater control will come with practise.
Again contact, hold for as long as you can without strain, relax.
Maximum contraction... and total relaxation. One round.
Continue for twenty rounds.

Ashwini Mudra (horse gesture)
Sit in any meditative pose, spine straight, head up.
Close your eyes.
Relax the body and maintain normal breathing.

Slowly contract the sphincter muscles of the anus for a few seconds.

The sensation is that of holding to prevent defecation.

Now relax for a few seconds.

Contract... relax... evenly and rhythmically.

You should contract only the anus.

Be careful that there is no movement of the urinary or genital systems.

Continue in this way for fifty rounds.

Then practise in time with the breath.

As you inhale, slowly contract the anal muscles.

At the peak of inhalation, hold the breath and the contraction.

The contraction should be as tight as possible without strain.

Register this sensation clearly and remember it.

Then slowly release as you exhale.

This is one round.

Practise twenty-five rounds.

Vajroli Mudra (thunderbolt attitude)

Siddhasana or siddha yoni asana is ideal but you may sit in any meditative pose, with the spine straight.

Close the eyes and relax the body.

Take your awareness to the genital region and try to locate the vajra nadi.

This nadi carries the sensation of physical bliss from the genitals to the brain. It also carries the impulses of blissful spiritual awakening up sushumna to sahasrara. In men this psychic channel has its physical counterpart in the urethra, the urinary passage within the penis. In women it originates at the clitoris, just above the urinary opening.

Try to find this nadi with your awareness.

Focus your attention on its physical counterpart until you become intensely aware of the pranic pathway itself.

Now contract vajra nadi.

Feel or imagine that you are trying to restrain urination. Then relax completely.

Again contract. Men will feel the penis draw back into the abdomen.

Women will feel the outer vaginal muscles and the hood of the clitoris move.

Try not to contract the other muscle groups in the pelvic floor.

If you are sitting in siddhasana/siddha yoni asana you will feel this contraction more directly.

In both sexes the anus and lower abdomen will also contract.This should be avoided or at least minimized.

Check that the rest of the body is unaffected.

Tighten vajra nadi... tighten... and release.

Rhythmic contraction and relaxation for twenty-five rounds.

Now combine this practice with awareness of the breath.

Take a long, deep breath in and gradually contract vajra nadi.

The point of maximum inhalation is the point of maximum contraction.

Hold it for an instant. Intense awareness of this sensation.

Then gradual controlled release.

This is one round. Practise twenty-five rounds.

Practice note: This is a simplified version of vajroli which helps one to slowly gain complete mental and physical mastery over the urogenital muscles and the vajra nadi. When complete mental and physical mastery over these muscles is achieved the practitioner may, with proper expert guidance, move on to the more advanced stages of vajroli.

Note: *Vajroli mudra is also known as* ojhi kriya.

Ashwini-Moola-Vajroli alternation

Sit in any meditation posture that applies pressure to the mooladhara trigger point. Siddhasana and siddha yoni asana are ideal. Rest the hands on the knees.

Become aware of the area surrounding the anus.
Focus your attention on the anus and slowly contract the anal muscles in ashwini mudra.
Rapid, rhythmic practise of ashwini mudra ten times.
Remember ashwini – its focus and its sensations.
Now move further inside the body to mooladhara trigger point.
Briefly contract and relax mooladhara.
Sthul moola bandha – ten rounds.
Know it and remember it. It is a more subtle, less physical practice than ashwini.
Move forward again and to the surface of the body.
Find vajra nadi.
Perform vajroli mudra.
Ten rounds – rhythmically, with awareness.
Clearly record the site and the sensation.
This is one rotation – ashwini, moola, vajroli.
Practise three complete rotations.
Now repeat this in time with the breath.
Five rounds of ashwini mudra with the breath, contracting as you inhale, release as you exhale.
Then five rounds of sthul moola bandha, inhale and contract, exhale and relax.
Then vajroli five times – tighten as you breathe in, release as you breathe out.
Then sit quietly and centre yourself in chidakasha.
Mentally perform one rotation, recalling the distinct sensation associated with each one.
Focus on the similarities... and the differences.
Check that you are practising each one independently, and not two or three together. Ashwini – moola – vajroli.
Know them thoroughly and their subtle distinctions.

Moola Bandha and Kumbhaka

Moola Bandha with Antar Kumbhaka (inner retention)

Sit in siddhasana, siddha yoni asana or any other comfortable posture that enhances awareness of the mooladhara trigger point.

Relax your body and close your eyes.

Witness the natural breath flowing in and out of your body.

Spontaneous, natural breath...

Now bring your awareness to mooladhara trigger point.

Expand your awareness to include both the breath and mooladhara.

Intense awareness, breath and mooladhara.

Now feel, or imagine, that as you breathe in you are drawing the breath up from mooladhara to ajna chakra in the mid-brain behind the eyebrow centre.

As you breathe out your awareness flows back from ajna to mooladhara.

Inhale from mooladhara to ajna.

Exhale from ajna to mooladhara.

Some people experience this movement of the breath straight up and down the spine, directly between mooladhara and ajna chakra.

Others feel it moving up the front of the body from mooladhara to the pubic bone, centre of the chest, throat, nosetip, to the eyebrow centre, and then down again.

Yet others experience the movement up the front of the body to ajna and down the spine to mooladhara.

This is a matter of personal sensitivity and preference. Simply choose your pathway and become aware of the movement of the breath along that pathway.

Inhale from mooladhara to ajna.

Exhale from ajna to mooladhara.

Your awareness should be exactly synchronized with the breath.

As you reach the peak of inhalation, your awareness reaches ajna chakra. The moment your awareness arrives at mooladhara, your exhalation should be complete.

Inhale from mooladhara to ajna.

Exhale from ajna to mooladhara.

You will notice that your natural breath has become slower and deeper. Now, at the peak of inhalation, in ajna chakra, hold your breath.

Bring the chin to the chest (jalandhara bandha). This will help you hold the breath.

Retain the breath in ajna for a comfortable length of time.

Then raise the head and take a short breath in, then slowly exhale down to mooladhara.

Inhale to ajna, chin to chest, hold the breath, raise the head, exhale to mooladhara.

Do not strain.

Do not over-extend your breath retention.

Maintain a relaxed, natural rhythm.

When your breathing pattern is established, add moola bandha.

As you breathe in, slowly contract mooladhara.

Draw the inhaled breath up from mooladhara while slowly tightening the contraction of the chakra. Make sure the rest of the body is relaxed.

Bring the chin to the chest.

The peak of inhalation at ajna is also the point of maximum contraction at mooladhara.

Hold it.

Then raise the head, and very slowly release the contraction as you breathe out.

The point of complete exhalation at mooladhara is also the point of total relaxation.

Breathe in, contracting mooladhara.

Chin to chest.

Hold the contraction and the breath in ajna.

Rotate your awareness between ajna and mooladhara.

Then simultaneous awareness of both.

Raise the head.

Breathe out to mooladhara and release the bandha.

This is one round.

Begin with three rounds and gradually build up to ten.

Allow your breath to return to normal after each round.

As you become established in this practice, you will spontaneously become more and more aware of the psychic dimension of moola bandha.

As you contract mooladhara, feel the psychic energy rising with the breath.

While holding the bandha, be aware of the powerful energy impulses fired from mooladhara and exploding in ajna.

As you breathe out, watch the dark space behind the forehead (chidakasha) and feel this vital energy diffusing throughout the body.

After completing your practice, sit with eyes closed in the same asana.

Rest your mind in the warm, friendly darkness of chidakasha, and allow yourself to be aware of your physical reactions.

How is your heartbeat?

What is happening with your breath?

Let every bodily sensation – pleasant or otherwise – come before your relaxed awareness....

Then move from your body to your feelings.

Does this practice arouse any special emotion?

94

Or memory?
Do you feel afraid, tearful, happy, exhilarated?
Watch the play of your sentiments as if you were watching
an actor on the stage.
Witness them with the objectivity of a news reporter.
Remember, in chidakasha there is nothing good and
nothing bad.
Simple awareness...
When both body and mind are tranquil, then chant *om*
mentally three times.
And end the practice, or move into your usual meditation
practice.

Moola Bandha with Bahir Kumbhaka (external retention)

Sit in siddhasana, siddha yoni asana or any other comfort-
able posture that enhances your awareness of the
mooladhara trigger point.
Relax your body and close your eyes.
Witness the natural breath flowing in and out of your
body.
Spontaneous, natural breath...
As you watch your breath, it will spontaneously become
slower and deeper.
At this point, take a deep breath in.
At the peak of inhalation, hold the breath for an instant.
Then breathe out fully, contracting the abdominal
muscles to empty the lungs completely.
As you breathe out, bring the head down until the chin
rests on the chest (jalandhara bandha).
When exhalation is complete, allow the abdominal
muscles to relax.
Just let them go – let them sag – relax.
Hold the breath outside the body.
Contract mooladhara and maintain the bandha for as
long as you can without strain.
When you are ready, raise the head, breathe out a
fraction, and then breathe in.

Release the bandha in time with the breath. Only when you have completely filled the lungs should you release the final pressure of moola bandha.

At the peak of inhalation hold the breath inside for an instant, then breathe out and relax.

This is one round.

Allow your breath to return to normal.

Now practise another round, this time intensifying awareness of the flow of prana.

Breathe in deeply and feel, or imagine, that you are drawing psychic energy up from mooladhara to ajna.

Hold the breath in ajna for an instant.

Breathe out fully, contracting the abdominal muscles.

Bring the chin to the chest, simultaneously experiencing the withdrawal of energy back to mooladhara.

Your exhalation is complete – relax the abdomen.

Your awareness is focused in mooladhara.

Hold the breath outside, and apply moola bandha.

Feel moola bandha redirecting the apana vayu so that it spontaneously flies upwards to mingle with the prana in manipura, the navel centre.

Visualize this union with respect and reverence.

Experience this union, a subtle initiation, a spiritual rebirth.

Raise the head, exhale slightly, and then inhale from mooladhara to ajna chakra while releasing moola bandha.

Experience the tremendous surge of power from mooladhara piercing through ajna, hold the breath for an instant at ajna, then breathe out and feel this energy gently diffusing throughout the body.

This is one complete round with both physical and pranic awareness.

Begin with three rounds and over several months build up to a maximum of nine rounds.

Allow the breath to return to normal after each round.

When your practice is complete, remain seated in the same asana with your eyes closed.

96

Rest your mind in the warm, friendly darkness of chidakasha, and allow yourself to become aware of each and every sensation in your physical body.
Feel your heartbeat.
Do you feel hot or cold?
What is happening with the breath?
Total awareness on the physical plane... and the emotional plane.
Does this practice awaken any particular feelings?
Do you feel fear, anxiety, sadness, relief, contentment, exhilaration?
Watch your feelings like sunlight and shadow beneath a tree, observe them as if they were being portrayed by an actor on the stage.
Remember, in chidakasha there is nothing good and nothing bad.
Simple awareness... of your physical self, emotional self, true, inner self.
When every dimension of your being is tranquil, chant *om* mentally three times, and end the practice.
Or move into your usual meditation practice.

Moola Bandha:
the Psychic Lock

Technique I – with Antar Kumbakha (internal retention)
Sit in siddhasana, siddha yoni asana or any other comfortable position that enhances awareness of mooladhara chakra.
Close your eyes and relax the whole body by watching the natural breath... in and out... natural breath.
Now take your awareness to mooladhara chakra.
Intense awareness of mooladhara.
Total attention at mooladhara, then breathe in deeply, hold your breath, and mentally contract mooladhara.
Contraction in the pranic body only – no physical contraction.
Complete physical relaxation but psychic contraction of mooladhara on the subtle plane.
Feel or imagine that the actual chakra is being lightly pressed with your thumb, or that mooladhara is being gently beaten with a flower, the psychic contraction of mooladhara chakra.
Repeat the seed mantra slowly and mentally: *lam... lam... lam...* and with each repetition feel the primal energy surging up from mooladhara.
When you can no longer hold your breath comfortably, breathe out slowly and feel the energy from mooladhara diffusing throughout the body and clearing the thoughts from the mind.

Sit quietly and experience the tranquil void in chid-akasha, the space behind the closed eyes
This is one round.
Practise up to twelve rounds and then proceed with your usual meditation practice.

Technique 2 – with Bahir Kumbakha (external retention)

Sit in siddhasana, siddha yoni asana or any other comfortable position that enhances awareness of mooladhara chakra.

Close your eyes and relax the whole body by watching the spontaneous flow of the natural breath...

Now expand your awareness to include mooladhara chakra. Awareness of the breath and intense awareness of mooladhara.

Now breathe in deeply and allow your awareness to flow up to ajna chakra in time with the breath.

At the peak of inhalation, hold the breath in ajna for an instant.

Then breathe out fully, and allow your awareness to flow back down to mooladhara.

Intense awareness of mooladhara.

Hold the breath outside the body, and mentally contract mooladhara chakra.

Psychic contraction only – no physical contraction.

Feel or imagine that the chakra is being lightly pressed with the thumb, or that mooladhara is being gently beaten with a flower.

Psychic contraction of mooladhara chakra.

Repeat the seed mantra slowly and mentally: *lam... lam... lam...*

And with each repetition feel the primal energy exploding from mooladhara.

Hold the breath for as long as you can comfortably, then slowly inhale, allowing your awareness to flow up to ajna on the 'tide of energy' surging up from mooladhara.

99

Hold the breath and the awareness for an instant in ajna, while the cascading energy clears all thoughts from the mind.

Then breathe out and relax in the pure void of chidakasha.

This is one round.

Practise up to twelve rounds and proceed with your usual meditation practice.

Maha Mudra

Technique

Sit in siddhasana or siddha yoni asana with the lower heel firmly pressing the mooladhara trigger point.

Make your spine straight, hold your head up and close your eyes.

Relax the whole body and become aware of your natural breath.

Spontaneous, relaxed breathing... in... and... out...

Now contract the throat slightly so your breath makes a gentle snoring sound as it passes in and out of the throat. A gentle rumble like a baby sleeping... like a waterfall in the distance... this is the psychic breath (ujjayi pranayama).

When you have become established in the psychic breath, fold your tongue backwards with the tip towards the throat.

The underside of the tongue rests against the roof of the mouth.

This is khechari mudra.

Deep, slow psychic breath and folded tongue... continue these throughout the practice. Now, the next time you breathe out, drop your chin to your chest (jalandhara bandha). Open your eyes.

Focus your attention on mooladhara chakra.

Hold the breath outside while you say mentally: 'mooladhara, mooladhara, mooladhara'.

101

Maha Mudra

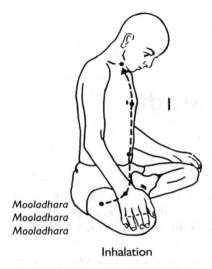

Mooladhara
Mooladhara
Mooladhara

Inhalation

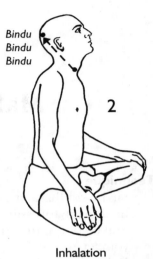

Bindu
Bindu
Bindu

Inhalation

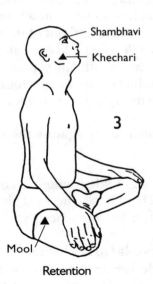

Shambhavi

Khechari

Mool

Retention

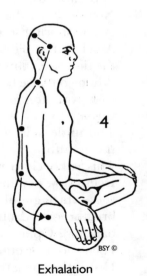

Exhalation

BSY ©

With the psychic breath, breathe in and draw your awareness from mooladhara up the front of the body, to the throat, then to bindu at the back of the head.

Breath and awareness should move together from mooladhara to swadhisthana at the pubic bone, manipura at the navel, anahata in the chest, vishuddhi in the throat, then directly back and up to bindu.

As your awareness moves from vishuddhi to bindu, lift the head slowly so that by the time you reach bindu, the head is tilted slightly backwards.

Head tilted back, breath and awareness simultaneously reach bindu.

Hold your breath.

Hold your awareness in bindu.

Repeat mentally 'bindu, bindu, bindu'.

Still holding the breath, focus your eyes on the eyebrow centre (shambhavi mudra).

And at the same time perform moola bandha.

Move your awareness to the eyebrow centre – say mentally 'shambhavi'.

Now take your awareness to the root of the tongue – say mentally 'khechari'.

Awareness of mooladhara chakra – say mentally 'moola'.

Again: 'shambhavi, khechari, moola'.

Third time: 'shambhavi, khechari, moola'.

Release shambhavi and then moola bandha.

Take your awareness back to bindu.

Exhale with the psychic breath and allow your awareness to descend through the psychic centres in the spine.

Synchronize breath and awareness, descending through ajna, vishuddhi, anahata, manipura, swadhisthana back to mooladhara.

At the same time, let your eyelids droop half-closed (unmani mudra).

Allow the head to drop forward slowly so that when your exhalation is complete, the chin rests on the chest again (jalandhara bandha).

Maha Mudra – Alternative Practice

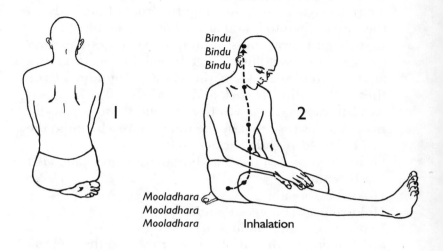

1

2

Bindu
Bindu
Bindu

Mooladhara
Mooladhara
Mooladhara

Inhalation

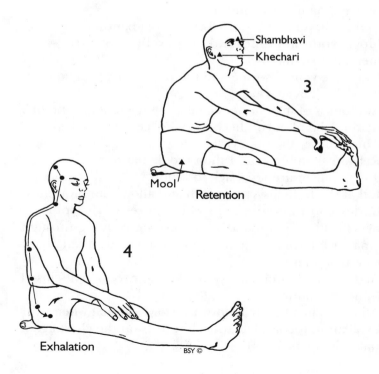

Shambhavi
Khechari

3

Mool

Retention

4

Exhalation

BSY ©

Awareness of mooladhara, eyes half-open.

This is the end of one complete round.

Mentally say, 'mooladhara, mooladhara, mooladhara'.

Breathe in with the psychic breath (ujjayi) and repeat as above.

Practise twelve rounds (i.e. twelve complete breaths).

Beginners should rotate their awareness – shambhavi, khechari, moola – three times.

Gradually build your practice up to twelve rotations with each breath.

This is the kundalini yoga kriya known as maha mudra.

Alternative practice

Maha mudra may also be practised in utthanpadasana or its variation.

Sit in utthanpadasana, or its variation, with the left leg folded and the right leg stretched in front of the body.

Rest the hands on the right knee, close your eyes and straighten your back.

Relax your whole body... and become aware of the natural breath...

Spontaneous, relaxed breathing...

Now contract the throat slightly so that your breath makes a gentle snoring sound as it passes in and out of the throat.

A gentle rumble like a baby sleeping... like a waterfall in the distance... this is the psychic breath (ujjayi pranayama).

When you have become established in the psychic breath, fold your tongue backwards with the tip towards the throat. The underside of the tongue rests against the roof of the mouth.

This is khechari mudra.

Deep, slow, psychic breath and folded tongue...continue these throughout the practice.

Now, the next time you breath drop your chin to your chest (jalandhara bandha), open your eyes.

Focus your awareness on mooladhara chakra.

Hold the breath outside while you say mentally 'mooladhara, mooladhara, mooladhara'.

With the psychic breath, breathe in and draw your awareness from mooladhara up the front of the body to the throat, then to bindu at the back of the head.

Breath and awareness should move together from mooladhara to swadhisthana at the pubic bone, manipura at the navel, anahata in the chest, vishuddhi in the throat, then directly up and back to bindu.

As your awareness moves from vishuddhi to bindu, lift the head slowly so that by the time you reach bindu, the head is slightly tilted backwards. Head tilted back, breath and awareness simultaneously reach bindu.

Hold your breath.

Hold your awareness in bindu.

Repeat mentally 'bindu, bindu, bindu'.

Bend forward and grasp the big toe of the right foot with both hands.

Keep the right leg straight, knee to floor.

Focus the eyes on the eyebrow centre (shambhavi mudra), and at the same time perform moola bandha.

Move your awareness to the eyebrow centre – say mentally 'shambhavi'.

Awareness at the root of the tongue – say mentally 'khechari'.

Awareness at mooladhara chakra – say mentally 'moola'.

Again: 'shambhavi, khechari, moola'.

Third time: 'shambhavi, khechari, moola'.

Release shambhavi mudra.

Release moola bandha.

Straighten the spine and rest the hands on the knees.

Come again to bindu, and with the psychic breath, breathe out through the spine.

Synchronize your awareness as it descends through all the psychic centres – ajna, vishuddhi, anahata, manipura, swadhisthana to mooladhara.

Breath and awareness should reach mooladhara together.

As you exhale, also let your eyes droop half-closed (unmani mudra).

Allow the head to drop forward slowly so that when your exhalation is complete, the chin rests on the chest again (jalandhara bandha).

Breathe out, awareness of mooladhara, spine straight, eyes half-open.

This is the end of one complete round.

Do four rounds with the right leg forward.

Then four rounds with the left leg forward.

Next, four rounds with both legs in front of the body.

This is the complete practice of maha mudra in utthanpadasana.

Appendix

Moola Bandha and Acupuncture

Acupuncture is an ancient Chinese healing system intimately related to Taoist philosophy which views everything in the universe as being an intermingling balance of the two primordial forces *yin* and *yang*. Together yin and yang represent every dichotomy in the dualistic world, e.g. black/white, night/day, pain/pleasure, and so on. Yin and yang respectively may also be said to represent a negative and a positive force. A balance between these two forces is an index in the body of sound health and general wellbeing.

Yin and yang combine to form what is called *chi*. This is somewhat similar to the yogic concept that ida and pingala are opposite aspects of prana. According to acupuncture theory, chi flows along energy pathways known as meridians, which correspond to the yogic nadis, and they carry chi to all the functional areas of the body. Of the 59 meridians, the 12 main meridians and the 8 extra meridians are of incomparably greater importance than the others. The body is a complex network of these meridians, and physical, mental and spiritual health is maintained by the unobstructed flow of chi through each of these energy channels.

When the body emits a signal (irregular pulse, overt physical or psychological symptoms) indicating the existence of a yin/yang imbalance, one or several of the 760 acupuncture points in the body is *piqued* (stuck with a needle) and balance is restored.

111

Now, 24 of these acupuncture points lie on one of the 8 extra meridians known as *Ren Mo* (conception vessel) while another 28 points lie on the extra meridian known as *Du Mo* (governing vessel). The governing vessel (Gv) begins at the tip of the coccyx (Gv 1)[1], and follows the course of the spine up over the centre line of the head, through the eyebrow centre (ajna chakra – Gv 24) down the ridge of the nose to the nosetip, terminating just below the insertion of the frenulum of the lip (Gv 28). The conception vessel (Cv) begins midway between the anus and the scrotum (the site of mooladhara chakra) with the point Cv 1. It then travels up along the centre line in front of the body to terminate in the lower lip Cv 24.

It is interesting to note that both the conception vessel and the governor vessel seem to correspond to the *arohan* and *awarohan* psychic passages visualized in kriya yoga. Kriya yoga seems to have been known in China, for a system which possesses many similarities are in a scripture called the *Tai Chin Hua Tzang Chih* (The Secret of the Golden Flower). The conception and governor vessels were imagined to run end to end to form an unbroken ellipse, and chi was visualized to travel in an anticlockwise fashion beginning at Gv1, circulating the body and ending at Cv 1 in the perineum. It has been argued by some critics that strictly speaking the ellipse is broken at the mouth (by the separation of the lips) and the perineal region (by the distance between the end of the coccyx and the centre of the perineum – approx. 5 centimetres). The Chinese argued however, that an internal connection exists via the alimentary canal, joining the mouth and the anus at the physical level, thus completing the circuit. It must be remembered that the vessels exist at the psychic plane which is not subject to physical limitations, and that the channels are continuous at this level.

It is not surprising that the pathways of the conception and governor vessels correspond exactly to the psychic pathways used in yoga meditation. But it is interesting to note that not only is Cv 1 the meeting point of the conception and governor vessels and the site for moola bandha, but in acupuncture theory it is also known as a *General Lo* point, through which any disequilibrium of yin and yang in the whole body (in particular the small intestines, heart, lungs, colon, bladder, kidneys, circulation and three heaters) can be rectified. As such it is an extremely important point, for by performing moola bandha not only is Cv 1 and, therefore, the whole of the conception vessel directly activated, but because of their interrelationship the governor vessel is also indirectly stimulated.

Both the conception (a yin meridian) and governor (a yang meridian) vessels are great reservoirs of chi. They supply the entire body with energy, and excess energy in turn is redistributed back to these vessels. Cv 1, by virtue of its connection with the governor vessel, is the seat of chi for the entire body in much the same way as mooladhara chakra is the source of kundalini.

In the *Nei Ying*, the chi generated in the conception vessel (and therefore Cv 1), for all the points of the meridian are interconnected) is described as "the non-erotic sexual energy that comes from the sexual organs, the energy of breathing, digestion and excretion".[2] On a yogic level this same non-erotic sexual energy is referred to as prana.

In his book *Le Traitement des Algies par l'Acupuncture* (The Treatment of Diseases through Acupuncture), J.E.H. Niboyet lists 19 different ailments that may be treated via the governor vessel.[3] Further, he lists another 29 physical complaints that may effectively be alleviated (directly or indirectly) by means of the conception vessel, which we now know is actively stimulated by moola bandha.[4]

The importance of the conception vessel does not end with its amazing ability to alleviate a wide range of physical ailments. In acupuncture there are what are termed 'centre reunion particular points'. These points have an effect upon the internal organs. Two such points lie on the conception vessel and are known as Cv 17 and Cv 12. At Cv 17 there is reunion of the 'breath energy' and it is an excellent point of all pulmonary diseases. It is possible now to understand how the stimulation of Cv 1(thereby activating Cv 17) through moola bandha may prove effective in the problems of asthma and bronchitis. At Cv 12 there is a reunion of the five *fu* (yang) organs – gallbladder, small intestines, stomach, colon and bladder, which may be used in cases of epigastric discomfort with hyperacidity. Now it is also reasonable to suggest that through the practice of moola bandha, it is possible (via Cv 12) to directly influence five of the major organs of the body.

The four seas

The *Nei Ying* says: "Man possesses four seas and twelve main meridians, which are like rivers that flow into the sea."

The four seas are the seas of nourishment, blood, energy and bone marrow. They are energy systems that supply the body with specialized capacities to maintain the internal, physical, mental or spiritual functions in man. Energy, to the Chinese, was an all-encompassing concept taken to include physical energy, mental energy and chi energy, right through to the subtlest, subatomic energies available to man through one human body. The sea of energy is physically represented by the region around the centre of the chest.[5] The conception vessel regulates and distributes this energy through Cv 17. If there is a fullness, a person feels pain in the chest, the face is red and there is breathlessness. If this sea exhibits signs of emptiness, the person cannot speak.

The sea of bone marrow has as its points of liaison an area localized on the top of the head at Gv 20.[6] The governor vessel is the controller of the sea of bone marrow, represented as brain tissue and a great storehouse for chi. If there is a fullness a person will feel that he has excess energy. If there is an emptiness a person will have dizzy bouts, hear noises in the ears, feel pain the calf muscles and have fainting spells.

Both the conception and governor vessels are great reservoirs of energy that alone support, maintain and regulate

114

two of the four seas of the body.[7] Through moola bandha one may also tap these seas, thereby assisting in maintaining total harmony within the organism, enervating it with vitality and longevity.

According to the Ma Chen-tai school of thought of the Ming dynasty, the meridians are compared to a river. The origin point, the first point on the meridian, is the source of the river, and the end point, the last point on the meridian, is the lake into which the waters of the river accumulate at the end of its course. Now, in relation to the conception vessel the accumulated waters of the spleen, kidney and liver meridians reside at Cv 12, Cv 23 and Cv 1 respectively. In other words, through the conception vessel and moola bandha it is possible to influence the functioning of the spleen, kidney and liver.

The windows of the sky
One of the most interesting sets of acupuncture points are those called the 'windows of the sky'. Again referring to the *Nei Ying* it says: 'All yang energies come from yin, for yin is earth. Yang energy always climbs from the lower part of the body towards the head; but if it is interrupted in its course it cannot climb beyond the abdomen. In that case one must find which meridian is diseased. One must tone (stimulate) the yin (as it creates the yang) and disperse (sedate) the yang so that the energy is attracted towards the top of the body and the circulation is re-established.'

The points used to perform this function are know as 'windows to the sky'. Two such points lie on the conception vessel at Cv 15 and Cv 22.[8]

There are three salient points that we may abstract from this passage:
1. Though the energies that move upwards from the lower extremities are yang, they are born from yin. The conception vessel is by nature yin. Yin is said to typify the earth element which is also symbolic of mooladhara chakra.

115

2. Both Chinese and yogic philosophy agree that the flow of energy is upward towards the top of the head.
3. On a physical level, the blocked rising chi in the abdomen is responsible for many stomach and intestinal disorders. On a pranic level it is said that the rising kundalini may have difficulty in piercing through blockages at manipura chakra situated behind the navel. However, it is further stated that once beyond manipura there is no possibility of the kundalini ever recoiling into mooladhara.

The significance of this for moola bandha essentially is that it can be used as a chi/prana regulator. It acts as a generator for the upward movement of yang chi and is especially beneficial in removing chi blockages.

Some confusion in the past has revolved around the possibility of awakening mooladhara chakra by means of *nasikagra drishti*. Now, with acupuncture theory the explanation is simple. Nasikagra drishti is a practice which essentially involves gazing at the nosetip. As already pointed out, the tip of the nose lies on the governor vessel which passes over the head and down the spine to terminate at the tip of the coccyx, Gv 1. As previously stated the mutual interrelationship between Cv and Gv 1 is such that if the governor vessel is stimulated (as it is psychically through nasikagra drishti) Cv 1 is also stimulated, triggering mooladhara chakra.

In the tantras it is written that ajna chakra (whose external focusing point is the eyebrow centre) is directly connected with mooladhara chakra. This link can be explained through the relationship of the governor and conception vessels. If any awakening takes place in ajna it also takes place in mooladhara, and vice versa.

It is worthwhile noting in passing that Gv 1 is also used in the treatment of haemorrhoids, chronic blenorrhagia (excessive discharge of mucus, gonorrhoea), intestinal haemorrhage, diarrhoea, vomiting, lumbar neuralgia and epilepsy.

The three heaters

Perhaps the most fascinating acupuncture concept of interest in our study of moola bandha is that of 'the three heaters' or the 'three burning fires'. The three heater meridian is one of the twelve main meridians and is one for which no allopathic correlation can be offered. As such the three heaters have the following functions:

1. *Shang Chiao*, the upper heater – the respiratory function.
2. *Chung Chiao*, the middle heater – the digestive function.
3. *Hsia Chiao*, the lower heater – the sexual and eliminative functions.

Generally these heaters are grouped together under the term tri-heaters. Their uninterrupted functioning is extremely important as it is only through the intermedium of the tri-heaters that the human organism can absorb and transfer the vital energy necessary for life. As such, the three heaters also seem to correspond with mooladhara, manipura and anahata chakras. The tri-heaters are interrelated in such a way that an effect on one also has an effect on the other two. In this way they are also self-regulating.

Moola bandha is primarily concerned with the lower heater, in stimulating the fire of both the urogenital and anal systems. Because the three heaters are mutually interrelated, stimulation of the lower heater by the practice of moola bandha also influences the middle and upper heaters, and in this way can be used in digestive and pulmonary disorders also.

With or without pranayama the practice of moola bandha generates physical and psychic heat in the body. This heat is necessary to burn up impurities, thereby revitalizing the system and creating a solid foundation for harmonious living and sound health.

Concluding remarks

Though many of the connections between the points of the conception and governor vessels and the internal organs may appear to be impossible, not only according to modern

117

allopathic theory but also to common sense, it is a matter of empirical fact that tested under controlled experimental conditions, manipulation of acupuncture points has a direct effect on the vital functions of the body. Stimulation or sedation of these points influences not only the internal organs and physiological functioning, but also subtle energy systems within the body, just now coming within the perimeters of modern science.

Though still somewhat at a loss as to the actual mechanics of the operation, medical scientists are showing considerable interest in acupuncture, especially in relation to anaesthesia. The mechanisms of acupuncture are somewhat obscure and require further scientific exploration and definition. However, acupuncture offers not only the possibility of a synthesis between Chinese thought and scientific theory, but also an underlying thread between Taoism and Yoga, further enhancing a more complete understanding of moola bandha.

Glossary

Abdomen – area between the pelvis and chest.

Abreaction – release of emotional energy, freeing the mind from neurotic activity.

Adrenal glands – endocrine glands situated on top of the kidneys involved in manufacture and distribution of adrenaline, cortisone and other hormones.

Ajna – the psychic centre (chakra) that is the seat of intuition situated in the mid-brain.

Alpha brain wave – brain waves of 7–13 cycles per second which are found during relaxation, early meditation, ESP and creative states of mind.

Amaroli – Yogic tantric practice in which urine is used internally or externally for mental and physical health.

Amenorrhoea – absence of stoppage of the menses.

Anahata – the heart chakra or psychic centre that is the root of all emotions; associated with psychic sounds heard in meditation; situated behind the breastbone.

Anal sphincter – ring of muscle fibres which open and close anal orifice.

Antar mouna – inner silence; a meditation practice which focuses the mind on the sensations and the thoughts.

Anus – end of the digestive tract.

Apana vayu – pranic forces below the navel governing urination, defecation, reproduction and all downward moving forces.

119

Asana – physical yogic posture; a comfortable position.

Autonomic nervous system – part of the peripheral nervous system controlling automatic internal functions of the body which do not require conscious control.

Bandha – lock designed to hold prana or psychic energy within certain areas of the body so that its force can be redirected and utilized; muscular and psychic contraction of perineal body, abdomen and/or throat.

Beeja mantra – seed mantra.

Bindu – psychic centre through which *om*, the cosmic sound emerges into manifest existence; a point; semen.

Bioenergy – prana.

Biofeedback – the scientific method utilizing machines to detect biological signals and to feed them back to conscious awareness, thereby allowing control of body and mind to take place.

Biorhythms – biological rhythms, for example, the cycles of heartbeat and breath.

Brahmacharya – sexual control; redirection of sexual energy; turning the mind to live in higher consciousness.

Brahma granthi – psychic knot situated at mooladhara chakra.

Brahma nadi – sushumna.

Brahmarandhra – aperture in the crown of the head.

Cardiac plexus – interconnected bunch of nerves situated behind the breast bone, corresponding to anahata chakra.

Carotid sinuses – specialized blood pressure receptors situated in the neck for detection and regulation of changes in blood pressure.

Cerebral cortex – thin layer of grey matter or cells on the surface of the brain.

Cervix – lower end of the uterus, at the top of the vagina.

Chakra – literally 'wheel or vortex'; major psychic centre in the subtle body, responsible for specific physiological and psychic functions.

Chidakasha – psychic space behind the forehead where all psychic events are viewed; the space of consciousness.

Clitoris – small elongated erectile body in front of the vagina and behind the urethra.

Dhyana – meditation.

Dysmenorrhoea – painful menstruation.

Endocrine gland – secretes its produce, a hormone, into the blood.

Gonads – testicles in males, ovaries in females.

Hormone – endocrine gland secretion controlling various aspects of body function.

Hypothalamus – area in mid-brain which controls pituitary gland, autonomic nervous system and associated functions, for example – water balance, food intake, body temperature, etc.

Ida nadi – moon nadi corresponding to the parasympathetic nervous system.

Indriya – faculty of sense.

Inguinal hernia – weakness and swelling in the abdominal wall of the male groin region.

Jalandhara bandha – chin lock.

Jnanendriya – organ of perception, five in number – eye, ear, nose, tongue, skin.

Karmendriya – organ of action, five in number – larynx, hand, foot, anus, organ of generation.

Kevala kumbhaka – spontaneous stopping of the breath which occurs in the highest state of consciousness.

Khechari mudra – folding the tongue back so that the tip touches the soft palate at the back of the mouth.

Kriya yoga – system of kundalini yoga, which works through the active quality of mind to one-pointed concentration or meditation.

Kumbhaka – breath retention.

Kundalini – manifested power of the universe.

Kunjal kriya – practice of vomiting water as a cleansing technique.

Laryngeal plexus – intersection of a group of nerves corresponding to vishuddhi chakra.

Leucorrhoea – vaginal discharge.

Limbic system – part of brain which acts between mind and body. Concerned with regulation of the autonomic nervous system, endocrine glands, emotions and certain aspects of behaviour.

Loka – plane of existence.

Lumbar – region of the back between chest and pelvis.

Lumbar neuralgia – nerve pain in the lumbar region.

Maha bandha – the great lock; combination of the three bandhas.

Mania – phase of mental disorder characterized by expansive emotional conditions e.g. elation, overtalkativeness, hyperaggression, etc.

Manic depressive – alternating between states of mania and depression.

Manipura – the psychic centre (chakra) situated at the solar plexus which is associated with vitality and energy.

Maruts – vital energies of the body.

Medulla oblongata – an inch-long prolongation of the spinal cord into the brain.

Menopause – literally means cessation of the reproductive cycle.

Meridians – pranic pathways; may be equated to nadis.

Metabolism – the processes, chemical and physical, by which the body is maintained.

Mooladhara – psychic centre (chakra) located at the perineum in males and the cervix in females which is the seat of sexual and spiritual energy.

Mudra – physical posture and mental attitude which controls the psychic and subtle body energies.

Nada – the four stages of sound from struck or spoken to transcendental.

Nadi – passageway for the flow of energy in the psychic body.

Nadi shodhana pranayama – also known as alternate nostril breathing; the breath for purifying the psychic network.

Nasikagra drishti – nosetip gazing.

Nerve plexus – intersection of a group of nerves.

Neurosis – emotional disorder.

Ojas – redirected sexual energy.

Parathyroid – endocrine glands which control potassium and calcium levels in the body.

Pelvic floor – perineum.

Penis – male excretory and generative organ.

Pharyngeal plexus – intersection of group of nerves at the back of the mouth; associated with vishuddhi chakra.

Piles – dilated, bleeding veins in the anus; haemorrhoids.

Pineal – endocrine gland situated above pituitary gland, concerned with sexual function. Sometimes called the seat of intuition; associated with ajna chakra.

Pingala – sun nadi; corresponding to sympathetic nervous system.

Pituitary – master controlling endocrine gland.

Pooraka – inhalation.

Prana vayu – vital energies of the body.

Pranayama – control of vital and psychic energy in the body.

Pratyahara – sense withdrawal.

Prostatic hypertrophy – enlargement of prostate gland (lies just behind the penis and underneath the bladder).

Prostatic plexus – intersection of group of nerves in the lower pelvis, which corresponds to mooladhara chakra.

Psychosomatic – interaction of mind and body.

Rechaka – exhalation.

Rectum – last 15 cm of the digestive tract.

Rudra granthi – the psychic knot situated at ajna chakra in the mid-brain.

Sacral/coccygeal plexus – group of nerves intersecting at end of spinal cord in the lower pelvis; corresponding to swadhisthana chakra.

Sadhaka – spiritual seeker.

Sadhana – spiritual practice for spiritual illumination and total health.

Sahajoli – Female equivalent of vajroli.

Sahasrara – the crown chakra.

Sahit kumbhaka – breath retention using willpower.

Samkhya – one of the six main philosophies of India.

Samsara – creation; illusion; the ocean of the world.

Scrotum – sac containing the testicles.

Sensory motor system – pertaining to nerves of sensing and nerves of action.

Shakti – primal energy, the female aspect of the cosmos.

Shambhavi mudra – the upturning of the eyes to focus on bhrumadhya, the eyebrow centre.

Shiva – mythological Hindu god representing the highest consciousness; the male aspect of the cosmos.

Siddhi – psychic power.

Solar plexus – intersection of a group of nerves in the abdominal region – the physical manifestation of manipura chakra.

Spermatorrhoea – leakage of sperm

Sushumna – the most important nadi, running up the spinal cord.

Swadhisthana – the chakra located at the level of the pubic bone, and associated with the gratification of the pleasure sense.

Tantra – the science in which knowledge is gained through expansion and liberation of consciousness.

Tattwa – principle, element.

Testosterone – the male sex hormone.

Thoracic – pertaining to the chest.

Thymus – endocrine gland situated near the heart which is involved in the immunization of the body from disease.

Thyroid – endocrine gland situated in the throat which is involved in the energy production of the body.

Turiya – a fourth state of consciousness where the mind is transcended; the highest consciousness.

Uddiyana bandha – abdominal lock.

Ujjayi pranayama – deep throat breathing, the 'psychic breath' which has subtle calming effect on the whole system; used in many meditation techniques.

Urethra – canal which excretes urine from the bladder.

Urogenital – pertaining to the urinary and genital organs.

Uterus – where pregnancy occurs – situated just above the vagina.

Vagina – birth canal.

Vajra nadi – pranic channel controlling sexual function.

Vajroli – spiritual practice of rechanelling sexual energy; contraction of vajra nadi.

Vestigeal gland – remnant of a gland

Vidya – spiritual knowledge.

Vipareeta karani – the inverted attitude which redirects the vital nectar (amrit), fallen from bindu to manipura, back through vishuddhi to sahasrara.

Vishnu granthi – psychic knot situated at anahata chakra.

Vishuddhi – psychic centre located at the throat; the chakra of purification.

Vyana – one of five pranas within the body.

Yantra – symbolic diagram utilized in tantra.

Yoni mudra – also known as 'shanmukhi mudra', closing the six gates of perception in the head.

References

The Three Bandhas

[1]Gopal K.S. Lakshmanan S., Batmanabne M., 'A Study of the Effect of Bandhas in Pranayama on Pulse Rate, Heart Rate, Blood Pressure and Pulse Pressure', *Yoga Life*, vol. 8, no. 1, Jan. 1977.
Gopal K.S., Anantharaman V., Balachander S., Nishith S.D., 'The Cardiorespiratory Adjustments in Pranayama With and Without Bandhas, in Vajrasana', *Ind. J. Med. Sc.*, vol. 27, no. 9, Sept. 1973.

[2]Gopal K.S. and Lakshmanan S., 'Some Observations on Hatha Yoga: An Anatomical Study', *Yoga Life* vol. 4, no. 1, Jan. 1973.

Appendix

[1]Gv is the governing vessel; Cv, the conception vessel. Numbers alongside designate the number of the acupuncture point found at the anatomical site stated in the text.

[2]Ilza Veith, *Nei Ying*, translated as *The Yellow Emperor's Classic of Internal Medicine.*

[3]J.E.H. Niboyet's list of diseases susceptible to treatment by means of the governor vessel include: tonsillitis, sore throat, mouth diseases, conjunctivitis, headache, senile dementia (mental deterioration in the elderly), cold extremities, hallucinations, lumbago, neuralgia (nerve pain) of forehead and eyebrows, and toothache.
Note: In some cases the treatment of the above diseases requires the points on the governor vessel to be treated in combination with one or more acupuncture points on another meridian.

[4]J.E.H. Niboyet's list of 29 diseases susceptible to treatment by use of the conception vessel include: pain in head and neck, dyspepsia

(impairment of the digestive function), eczema (skin disease), emphysema (stretching of air sacs in the lungs), epilepsy, aphonia (loss of voice), breast abscess, asthenia (lack or loss of energy or strength), asthma, mouth disease, bronchitis, convulsions, common cold, pharyngitis, cough, hot flushes, whooping cough, diabetes, sneezing, influenza, haemoptysis (coughing of blood), laryngitis, meningitis of children, pleurisy and pneumonia, rhinitis and hay fever, sinusitis and pulmonary TB.

Note: In some cases, treatment of the above diseases requires combinations of points of the conception vessel and other meridians.

[5]This energy correlates with the sub-prana of mahaprana called *prana*, located between the diaphragm and the throat.

[6]The point corresponds roughly to bindu at the posterior fontanelle of the skull.

[7]The 'sea of nourishment' is controlled by the stomach meridian and the 'sea of blood' by the penetrating vessels.

[8]It seems that the Chinese, in formulating the 'windows of the sky' were also commenting on chi flowing from the trunk and legs to the top of the head. Refer to the chapter on *Pranic Effects*.

Bibliography
and Further Reading

Bentov I., 'Micromotion of the Body as a Factor in the Development of the Nervous System', published in *Kundalini – Psychosis or Transcendence?* Dr Lee Sannella, pub. by Lee Sannella, San Francisco, USA, 1976.

Bernard T., *Hatha Yoga*, Rider and Company, London, 1970.

Campbell J., *The Mythic Image*, Princeton Uni. Press, Princeton, 1974.

Courtois F., *An Experience of Enlightenment*, Shunju-sha, Tokyo, 1970.

Gopal K.S. & Lakshmanan S., 'Some Observations on Hatha Yoga: Bandhas, an Anatomical Study', *Ind. J. Med. Sc.*, 26:9:1972.

Gopal K.S., Anantharaman V., Balachandar S. & Nishith S.D., 'The Cardio-Respiratory Adjustments in Pranayama With and Without Bandhas; in Vajrasana', *Ind. J. Med.Sc.*, 27:9:1973.

Gopal K.S. & Lakshmanan S., 'Radiological Studies of Bandhas in Pranayama', *Medicine and Surgery*, XIV:3:1974, p. 5–7.

Gopal K.S. & Lakshmanan S. & Batmanabne, 'A Study of the Effect of Bandhas in Pranayama on Pulse Rate, Heart Rate, Blood Pressure and Pulse Pressure', *Yoga Life*, Vol. 8, No. 1, Jan 1977.

Iyengar B.K.S., *Light on Yoga*, George Allen and Unwin Ltd., London, 1972.

Jung C.G., 'Psychological Commentary on Kundalini Yoga', *Spring*, 1975.

Krishna G., *Kundalini: The Evolutionary Energy in Man*, Shambhala, Berkeley, 1971.

Krishna G., *Science and Kundalini*, paper presented at the Seminar on Yoga Science and Man, New Delhi, 1975.

Kuvalayananda Swami, *Pranayama*, Popular Prakashan, Bombay, 1966.

Kuvalayananda Swami, *Asanas*, Popular Prakashan, Bombay, 1971.

Lawson-Wood D. & I., *Five Elements of Acupuncture and Chinese Massage*, Health Science Press, England, 1973.

Leadbeater C.W., *The Chakras*, Theosophical Pub. House, 1972.

Mann F., *Acupuncture, the Ancient Chinese Art of Healing*, Random House Inc., NY, 1963.

Mann F., *Acupuncture, the Ancient Chinese Art of Healing and How it Works Scientifically*, Vintage Books, NY, 1972.

Mishlove J., *The Roots of Consciousness*, Random House Inc., NY, 1975.

Mookerjee Ajit, *Tantra Art*, Ravi Kumar, New Delhi, 1972.

Muktananda Swami, *The Play of Consciousness*, Shree Gurudev Ashram, Campbell, Ca, USA, 1974.

Narayananda Swami, *The Primal Power of Man*, Prasad & Company, Rishikesh, India, 1960.

Reich W., *The Function of the Orgasm*, Panther, UK 1968.

Rieker,H ., *The Yoga of Light, Hatha Yoga Pradipika*, The Dawn Horse Press, California, 1971.

Rosenberg J.L., *Total Orgasm*, Random House Inc., USA, 1975.

Rycroft C., *Reich*, Collins, London, 1971.

Sannella L., *Kundalini – Psychosis or Transcendence?* Pub. by Lee Sannella, San Francisco, USA, 1976.

Sargant W., *Battle for the Mind*, Pan, London, 1970.

Sargant W., *The Mind Possessed*, William Hunemann.

Satyananda Swami, *Kundalini Tantra*, Bihar School of Yoga, Munger, India, 1972.

Satyananda Swami, *Four Chapters on Freedom – Commentary on Yoga Sutras of Patanjali*, Bihar School of Yoga, Munger, India, 1976.

Satyananda Swami, *Meditations from the Tantras*, Bihar School of Yoga, Munger, India, 1977.

Satyananda Swami, *Asana Pranayama Mudra Bandha*, Bihar Yoga Bharati, Munger, India, 1996.

Sivananda Swami, *Science of Yoga Vol. 4*, Divine Life Society, Rishikesh, India, 1971.

Veith Ilza, *The Yellow Emperor's Classic of Internal Medicine*, Uni, of California, USA, 1973.

Vyasdev Swami, *Science of Soul*, Yoga Tibetan Trust, India, 1964.

Wilhelm R., *The Secret of the Golden Flower, a Chinese Book of Life*, Harcourt, Brace and World, NY, 1962.

Woodroffe Sir John, *The Serpent Power*, Ganesh & Co., Madras, India, 1964.

Wychoff J., *Wilhelm Reich, Life Force Explorer*, Faucett, Greenwich, USA, 1973.

Yogeshwarananda Swami, 'Awakening Kundalini is Just the Beginning', *I.A.R.P. Newsletter*, Institute for Religion and Psychology, Tokyo, 1977.

Index of Practices

Notes

—————————————— Notes ——————————————